LandBook

by Neil Shelton

D1501350

First Print Edition

To the lovely and mysterious Olga

Introduction

The Earth is a beautiful and wondrous place which contains… well, everything on earth. However, one thing it has not contained, until now, is an Owner's Manual.

Of course Earth doesn't have a single owner, and those that own the largest parts of it don't seem to be in need of any instruction, but my goal in writing this book was to benefit some of the Earth's smallest shareholders, those folks who own small acreages whose goals were not political or financial world domination, but a simpler, healthier, more autonomous lifestyle for themselves and their families.

In my four decades of dealing with these sorts of properties, I've discovered that there are any number of ways to approach purchasing and managing rural real estate if one has a bountiful supply of cash, but, having never found myself in that particular position, I wanted to share some of the knowledge and techniques I've learned for those folks who can't afford to hire a specialist for every need.

My goal isn't to teach the reader to be his or her own attorney, broker, surveyor, or excavation contractor. Rather, I'd like to show you how to do the things you can for yourself, and how to recognize the things that require professional help. We'll cover how to buy and sell land in ways that are both ethical and profitable, how to measure and locate your boundaries for your own purposes, and what to expect when you hire a well driller. You'll learn things you can do now that will save you from needing an attorney later, how to maintain a long, unpaved driveway for yourself, and quite a bit more.

In short, this is a handbook for your land, a LandBook, if you will. I hope you enjoy it.

Neil Shelton

Table of Contents

Chapter 1: Choosing Land

Of all the things on Earth that money can buy, none of them quite compare to the earth itself, that is, to land.

There are two types of property on Earth: land, and the things permanently affixed to it, which we Earthlings call "real" property, and everything else, which we refer to as "chattel", or personal property. The distinction between these two may seem elemental and unimportant, but it points to some valuable advice about how to manage our lives and our land.

That's because land that we own isn't just another bauble that passes through our hands. Land ownership can be compared to marriage, because, like marriage, a wise land-purchase can be one of the most stabilizing influences we humans can introduce into our lives, or under the wrong circumstances, one of the biggest mistakes we can make.

In fact, buying land in partnership with someone else can have very similar consequences to marrying that person, in that ending the partnership can be both painful and costly.

Like marriage, owning land allows us to put down roots, which is probably a good thing, but it also ties us to our decisions, some of which may, or may not, be in our own best interests.

Owning land looks good on our financial statement, and it can provide us with collateral to borrow money. Land can be a good investment, and it can be a source of income of itself. It can give us avenues to more personal autonomy and independence. As property owners we can control our personal environment: we can plant or plow, dig or fill, build or bulldoze according to our whims.

Unlike anything else we may own, land will always be there, right in the same location subject only to the movements and existence of Earth itself. We can't misplace it, we can't wear it out, and even though we may damage it severely, or improve it markedly, we can't take it somewhere else, or destroy it.

It would be difficult to imagine how someone could exaggerate the importance of land because virtually every human endeavor requires it in one way or another. Even if you live in a yellow submarine, or on a space station, you have to have a place to dock and replenish supplies occasionally.

However, as with the weather, most people in the modern world don't give a lot of thought to the part of the earth that they occupy; the cubical worker spends each day in essentially the same environment as he spent the one before, all but oblivious to rain and snow, soil and rock, for these things rarely intrude into his climate-controlled existence. Likewise, the suburbanite may take a moment every so often to poison the dandelions that intrude through cracks in his driveway, or he may even take the time to plant the occasional ornamental shrub or shade tree, but when he bought his property, far more thought went into the home, the school district, the distance from shopping centers, or any of dozens of other considerations that seemed more important than the actual land he would be living on.

The outstanding exception to this rule, is the small land-owner. Call him a homesteader, a small-holder, hobby-farmer, or what you will, this is a man or woman intensely interested in the land he or she owns, and every aspect about it.

This book is about the sort of land that that sort of landowner values most. These low- budget, family-oriented individuals have certain needs and wishes to fulfill in their choice of land, and these requirements are as different from the modern-day "farmer", who in many cases has become more of a corporate, semi-industrial entity, as they are from the urban or suburban property owner.

While I wouldn't presume to tell anyone what they might *want* in the way of property, there are several aspects that the small land-holder will want to take into consideration when he chooses rural land.

Size: Unlike the quasi-corporate agri-farmer, the small landowner strives for self- sufficiency in all ways possible, so he, or she, or they, probably won't be concentrating all of their efforts toward production of large amounts of only one or two crops. Rather, the desire is for a comfortable place to live on which they can produce many of the things their lifestyle requires in an environment that is at once cleaner, safer, more visually appealing, and which provides a life with privacy and personal autonomy. They'll want a garden, which doesn't require a great deal of land, say one half to one acre typically, and they may also want to raise a few head of livestock for the family's personal use, which will require a significant amount more land, perhaps five to ten acres or more. Ideally, they'll also want to make most of their income on this land which could require from ten acres for specialty crops up to forty or more for livestock …or not – they may make a living in a home studio, or shop, or on the internet.

In fact, even though the perennial question posed by prospective real estate buyers is, "how much land do I need to pasture, garden, etc." the truth is that it's impossible to say that anyone "needs" any certain amount of acreage, because we are all individuals doing things our own way, and besides that, once we decide what the minimum acreage would be, we'll discover someone getting it done with less.

Even a single acre can be made quite productive using techniques such as intensive planting and vertical gardening, and by using dwarf cultivars or smaller species of livestock. For example, in studies done by the University of California at Davis, researchers found that dwarf peach trees planted at the rate of 1,500 per acre – that's a tree for every 5.4 square feet – could produce 30 tons of fruit per acre by the third year. I leave it to the reader to visualize what 60,000 pounds of peaches would look like, but suffice it to say, it's a lot of fruit to harvest from a 208- foot square.

It's also probably more peaches than the typical family is likely to consume in a year, but by applying this sort of efficiency to a well-balanced operation including fruits, vegetables, and livestock, some resourceful folks have managed to provide everything to sustain their family's food habits on even a small city lot.

To be honest, while small land-holders typically value efficiency over waste and excess, most folks would prefer not to be that crowded, and the vast majority of them want privacy and a little room to wander in peace and quiet just about as much as they want groceries. So when all is said and done, the size of the acreage people typically settle on is mostly determined by what they can afford. In this regard, more is almost universally considered better than less.

Shape: Most people seem to prefer parcels of land that tend to be as close to square as possible, perhaps so that they can insulate themselves from whatever may be happening on neighboring properties by situating their living quarters in the middle of the parcel. This certainly has its advantages, but you may find it more appropriate to react to the neighboring situations that actually exist by locating on the side of the property furthest from any potential nuisance. For example, if your property adjoins an old-fashioned hog farm (something in itself well worth avoiding in the selection process) then sooner, or later, you'll probably opt to locate your home as far from the hog huts as possible.

In areas of Europe where a great deal of the land is flat, and much row-crop farming is done on small tracts using relatively small tractors — or even draft animals — such as is the practice in some parts of Poland and the Netherlands, land tends to be divided into long, thin strips that make for long runs and few turn-arounds by the plowman (Figure 1). (The word "furlong" now refers to a distance of 1/8 mile, but it originally simply meant a long furrow.) On the other hand, The United Kingdom and Ireland have many small farms devoted to pasturing animals, and these properties tend to be more even on all sides (square to round) so as to keep the animals close to home and minimize the amount of fencing required (Figure 2).

Terrain and Soil: Unless a property is nearly flat, the terrain will be an important factor to consider. In hilly country, you can expect the best soil to be in the low-lying areas, second- best will be the level hill-tops, and then you'll probably find that the hillsides have very little topsoil at all. This of course, is because of the flow of rainwater, and thus erosion, which is another consideration to keep in mind when shopping for land. Crop farming is probably best done in the bottoms, whereas a hilltop is often the best place for an orchard as air drainage will protect such areas from frosts. Gardeners used to prefer bottom-land also, but more and more gardening is done intensively in raised beds, so a location closest to the home is more desirable regardless of the soil conditions at that particular spot.

When locating a home or buildings, it's good to remember not just that bottomland can be muddy and that water will pool during wet times, but that the lower part of a hill may quickly saturate to the point of instability after a rainstorm. Even if your soil isn't so unstable that mudslides occur, water collecting in the surface soil near the bottom of a long slope can result in an area where navigating a four-wheel-drive, or even attempting foot traffic up and down the slope can become near to impossible

Beyond this, you'll want to think of the prevailing winds. On a sunny day in winter, a home-site that is shielded to the north and west by terrain will be much more comfortable than a hill-top or plain in most locations – something to think about before you build in sight of that stunning view you enjoy on balmy spring days. A southern-exposed location will also provide you with the most direct sunlight, so this will probably be the easiest location at which to heat your home in winter. Also, if you locate your driveway up a south-facing slope, snow and ice will melt off faster there.

On the other hand, northern slopes generally hold more moisture and erode less, so these are the areas where the timber grows best, and as a rule of thumb, you'll find the better species of trees growing on north-facing hillsides. Any part of your access road that crosses a north slope may stay impassible in severe winter weather for days longer than will the southern slope.

[BELOW] Crop land in the Netherlands

Figure 1 © 2013 Google; Aerodata International

[BELOW] Pasture land in Wales, UK

Figure 2: © 2013 Google; Getmapping plc

Meteorological experts will tell you that a tornado can occur anywhere, but even so, it's not a bad idea to remember that tornadoes tend to move from the southwest to the northeast and typically jump over deep hollows, particularly those perpendicular to the storm's direction of travel.

Forest: Open ground may be good for row-crop farming, or pasture, but there are some ways in which it doesn't make such an attractive environment to live in. Having some forested areas on the homestead provides a number of advantages: first, forest provides a source of income. Now let me hasten to say that selling timber from a small property is fraught with risk. Even if you are treated fairly — and there are a number of ways that an unscrupulous logger can take advantage of you — you will probably not get enough money to make up for the loss of your timber in the long run. A tract of land that has been logged heavily can take decades to return to its original state – you may not live that long — and if the money you get for your trees looks meager today, imagine how it will seem after twenty or thirty years of inflation.

On the other hand, if you keep your trees for yourself, you will enjoy wild nuts, fruits such as persimmon and paw-paws, as well as the wild mushrooms and berries that choose the forest as their home. You'll have an effective natural wind-break to buffer the winter winds and shade to reduce the summer temperatures.

Your own forest can provide you with privacy, even if you only have a small tract of land, as well as a place to wander, learn, and reflect. It can also provide you with hunting ground if that's something that interests you, and even if you're not a hunter, hunting leases have become more lucrative for the property owner in recent years as the constantly-diminishing amount of forested land is shared by constantly increasing numbers of hunters.

Loggers eager to buy your timber will tell you that big trees will just go rotten in the centers and die if they're not cut, and there is an element of truth to this. However, if you leave them uncut, you will develop a forest of large old trees most of which will outlive you by decades – maybe centuries. During that time, your forest will be creating oxygen and sequestering carbon dioxide so you'll be doing considerably more to preserve the Earth than the most environmentally-conscious apartment-dweller. In fact, it has been estimated by those who choose to concern themselves with such things, that an acre of forest produces enough oxygen to keep 18 humans happily inhaling and exhaling all day long.

Water: There is a certain undeniable quality about a flowing stream of water, and all things being equal, most everyone would prefer to have one on their property. Unfortunately, all things are rarely equal, and among these unequal things is the price of land including or adjoining some water feature, versus the price of a similar, but drier property in the same neighborhood.

If you have decided that you absolutely must have a stream or lake frontage on the property you buy, well, that's how I felt too, and I've never regretted it, but you need to look at it the way you would a piece of art. You're paying for the aesthetic appeal, and since you are, you may as well prepare for the fact that you will pay significantly more for that property than the utility of the body of water is worth in crude terms of cash value. If you're looking for land in an area with an accessible water table, then you'll find a drilled well to have a much more practical value, and in all likelihood a lower price, than that idyllic little brook of your dreams.

Additionally, there are a few other cautions to be considered as well.

Owning frontage on a lake or large stream usually means you'll need to be prepared to share these benefits with the general public. It's a rare lake indeed which does not come with the sound of people and motorboats, especially during the summer months, and in most "navigable" streams, fishermen and others may have a legal right to come wading through your property, even if they aren't allowed on the shore*. To learn more about such matters than most people care to know, search the internet for "riparian rights".

Also, if you have but a few acres, you need to make very certain exactly how high the water can be expected to rise during times of flooding before you locate a home or other significant improvements. You also need to determine that such improvements are even permitted under local regulations.

Springs and smaller streams have many of the benefits to the small landowner that larger bodies have, but not so many of the drawbacks. However, you also need to remember that in times of severe drought, that is, when you may need water the most, your spring or brook may not be there to provide for you.

Conversely, small streams (and even dry-washes or arroyos) are notorious for flash-flooding. If sufficient watershed exists, a small stream can swell to ten or twenty times its normal width after only a few minutes of heavy rain with dire consequences for those unprepared downstream.

When it comes to providing potable water for a farmhouse or homestead, you would be well advised to drill a well if it is at all possible - even if your location is next to a large spring. Natural water sources are rarely reliable enough for home use, certainly not for the sort of use that the modern lifestyle requires, and they may need extreme filtration. Much has been written by well-meaning authors about ways to provide water to the home by other means, and of course there are plenty of places where wells are either impractical or impossible, but if the option is available to you, you can't make a better investment in the success of any rural undertaking than the money spent in drilling a modern deep well.

See Chapter 8 for more on drilling a well.

As mentioned above, streams and springs will tend to greatly increase the monetary value of a property. So, to a lesser degree will a stock pond, or what they call a "tank" in the southwest US: a deep, man-made depression in the earth designed to hold water.

Ponds may be spring-fed, or not. To be legitimately spring-fed, at least in the mind of a real estate agent, a pond only needs to have within it what may have only been a seepy, wet-spot in the grass before the pond was dug, and of course it's hard to say what it *used* to be after it's underwater. If there's a really large spring feeding a pond, that will be obvious because the water will be cleaner and less opaque.

You will probably pay a little more to get a property with a pond, but I hope you won't pay a lot more because frankly, in most cases it isn't really worth all that much. If the soil on your land has sufficient clay content and no shallow rock outcroppings, then the chances of your being able to successfully dig a pond are very good. If there are lots of ponds in the neighborhood of your property, then you can probably hire a bulldozer or track loader to dig one in a day or two, depending on how large you want your pond to be.

So, because unlike natural streams, stock ponds can be created, they probably aren't worth a great deal of extra cost. On the other hand, if there is any profit motive behind your calculations, having a pond dug will probably increase the value of the property by several times what it costs.

See Chapter 9 for more on ponds.

Access: During the back-to-the-land movement in the 70's, there were lots of folks who had lived in an urban or suburban environment all their young lives, and who were now reacting, or possibly over-reacting, to this by moving out into the woods - *way out into the woods*. They often wanted to be about as far from civilization as the locale had to offer.

I might have even been a little guilty of this myself, because even though I've been living here, 18 miles from town, since 1977, I would have to say that if I were only five miles from the little town that my mail comes out of, I'd have just about as much privacy as I do now, and I'd have saved quite a bit on gasoline over the decades.

On the other hand, I've never felt especially isolated here. (My kids complained about our location when they were growing up – to which I always responded, "Look, when you're a parent, you can live any place *your kids want to* if that's your desire." They never seemed to appreciate my wry irony.)

Back in the 70's, I did know people who moved as far, or further, from town as I am, but instead of that distance being a paved highway, they were fifteen or twenty miles out on a gravel road. Not only were they spending extra for gasoline, but they had to pay more for tires and repairs as the rough roads tend to harbor sharp rocks and vibrate nuts and bolts loose. I will acknowledge that had someone located 15-25 miles from a large city forty years ago, they would probably be living in suburbs now, but most rural areas do not exhibit this sort of rapid growth.

At any rate, the access into your land is perhaps one of the less obvious things worthy of a little concern. The distance you are from town becomes much less of a problem, gasoline costs notwithstanding, when the roads are paved.

If the roads aren't paved, then you want to give particular concern to who will be maintaining them, if anyone. If they aren't maintained by a government body, then the best assumption is that they won't be maintained at all, in which case, the simplest solution is to maintain them yourself. That doesn't need to be as difficult as it may sound to someone accustomed to having a street and sidewalk just outside the front door, but it does require a little bit of capital investment in equipment, and the time and knowledge required to use it.

See Chapter 6 for more on maintaining your own roads.

Perhaps the most important concern about access, as well as the least obvious, is the legality of any private road that passes through neighboring property. While a road that has been in continuous use for a certain period of time may be said to be a "prescriptive easement", you're a lot less likely to be defending your right to access your own property if you have a deeded easement recorded at the county, and the best time to make certain of this is *before* you've bought the property. If you have to go to court to keep your driveway, the law generally supports the property owner's right to access his property by the shortest route, (which your existing route may not be) but aside from the expense, like any other time you engage in litigation, your future is in the hands of the court, and dependant on the sympathy, compassion, wisdom, and sobriety of the judge. Nothing will make you appreciate the simple authority of a deeded easement like wasting a few months of your life and several thousands of dollars in a court battle just to get something you thought you had to begin with.

Price: By their very definition, small-holder properties are not lavish estates or desirable business locations, and typically they fall in the lower end of the scale as far as cost is concerned. However, land is rarely cheap, except in retrospect, and buyers of small tracts can expect to pay more per acre, perhaps a good deal more, than will large-acreage farmers – all the more reason to get the most from the land that you do have. By far the best, and most popular way of acquiring land is to inherit it, but many of us have neither the opportunity, nor the patience for this approach.

Did I just use the term "per acre"? Gosh, I wish I'd stop doing that. Price-per-acre may be a very significant consideration when buying large tracts, but on the sorts of small properties we're discussing here, I hope the reader won't pay it too much mind.

One of the reasons I recommend ignoring anything you read on an internet forum is because when the subject turns to land prices, there's always some nameless, faceless, clueless individual who knows nothing about the subject, and this is the guy who'll advise anyone silly enough to ask his opinion of a property they just bought. He'll say something like, "Any idiot knows (remember, this is the internet) that you can buy land cheaper than [whatever price was mentioned] Everyone knows that land around that area is selling for [whatever it was selling for 30 years ago] *per acre*."

Don't ever listen to this advice. If you'll just peruse a few dozen similar pieces of property on the market, you'll have a pretty good idea of what land is selling for in your area, and it won't be based on a per-acre price, but rather will reflect what the individual property has to offer. While the price that 5,000 acres sells for may have some distant relationship to what 5 acres sells for, it won't be very significant.

That brings up a companion error that occurs frequently. I often talk to people who tell me that they don't want anything that's part of a subdivision. Everything in America, I tell them, is part of a subdivision (of the Louisiana Purchase). What they're really trying to say, is that they want to buy an acre, or 5, or 10 out in the middle of nowhere surrounded by some large property, preferably something owned by the government. I can't say that such places don't exist, but you might have more luck in looking for Diogenes' honest man. As a rule, people, including the federal government, don't care to pare off a tiny slice of their huge acreages for the benefit of some guy who just wants to be alone. In other words, if Mr. Moneybags owns 900 acres for which he paid $2,000 per acre, can you expect him to sell you one acre for $2,000. No. $10,000? Well, maybe, but you can't expect to be his only customer.

The basic financial fact of land is that there are more people being born every day, and about the same amount of land available to them all, so barring a plague or famine, we can probably expect land prices to only go up in the long-term future. The major recession of 2009 proved that even a global turn-down in business won't slow the price of land appreciably, so if you're not lucky enough to be alive during a major cataclysmic world catastrophe, there's just not much you can do about the high price of land.

You can, however, do a few things to see that you buy the land you want for as small an amount money as is humanly possible, and I'll discuss a few of these techniques in the next chapter.

*"[T]he U.S. Supreme Court in 1979 created four tests for determining what constitutes navigable waters. Established in *Kaiser Aetna v. United States*, 444 U.S. 164, 100 S. Ct. 383, 62

Ed. 2d 332, the tests ask whether the body of water (1) is subject to the ebb and flow of the tide, (2) connects with a continuous interstate waterway, (3) has navigable capacity, and (4) is actually navigable. Using these tests, courts have held that bodies of water much smaller than lakes and rivers can also constitute navigable waters. Even shallow streams that are traversable only by canoe have met the test." - *The Free Dictionary by Farley*)

Chapter 2: The Basics of Purchasing Land

While it may be true that buying land is quite a bit more complicated than pumping your own gas, it becomes a lot easier if you know what all the steps are, which ones you perhaps won't need to concentrate on, and when, or if, you may wish to hire a professional.

Each land transaction has a few basic ingredients, rather like a bowl of bean soup (Okay, bear with me on this). In the most rural and backward locales, these basics are about all that you have to deal with. We can liken this situation to a bowl of beans and water. As things progress to rather more sophistication, we add things that cost a bit more, but make the overall experience better, such as title insurance, escrow services, and perhaps a building inspection. These benefits

in our increasingly silly soup metaphor – we can compare to salt, onion, and perhaps a little exotic seasoning. Finally, as this sophistication grows into unrestrained bureaucracy, we encounter various forms of perhaps unnecessary, but mandatory, complication, in which our soup takes the form of additives, preservatives and various polysyllabic concoctions the purposes of which are far beyond our ability to even imagine.

It may help you to remember this when shopping in different areas during your land- buying quest: things are extremely simple in the most undeveloped places, perhaps too simple in fact for our own safety, and in the largest population centers, things can be depended on to be mind-numbingly complex. Our goal should be to find the optimal condition. That is, the savory bean soup, between reckless negligence and infuriating complication.

So let's begin with the beans and water as it were, the Basic Requirements of Transferring Ownership of Land from a willing seller to a willing buyer.

These are: a medium of exchange, be it cash, property of value, or love and affection, and, a Warranty Deed.

…And that's all you really need, something to induce the seller to want to sell to the buyer, and a document that accomplishes the transfer of ownership, although as our soup at this point would benefit from a little salt and perhaps some spice, so will our land transaction be more palatable if we take a few steps further.

Some real estate transactions can actually be this simple. If, for example, your mother, who you may know to be an honest and reliable person, decides that because she loves you so, she wants to give you the present of a parcel of land that you know has been in the family for generations. Under these circumstances then, you probably don't need to be too concerned about being ripped off, although even then, there is one particular precaution that you need to take.

That is to record your deed. That's because while your deed does convey full ownership of the land from the moment it is signed, even while that document is resting in your pocket, it can easily be lost, or someone else might make a claim on the property, so you need to record your deed at the County Recorder's Office. They'll make a copy of your deed, which they will file in chronological order in their record books, then they'll charge you a small fee, and that establishes you as the "Owner of Record". The county will send their annual real estate tax bill to you, the next ownership plat will show your name or initials proudly emblazoned on your very own land, and any claims made on the property after the date of recording will be subordinate to yours.

Unfortunately, you may find yourself buying land from people who may not be quite as steadfast and trustworthy as one's dear Mum, and in that instance, you need to take certain additional precautions. For example, it would be a very good idea, before money changes hands, if you first determine that the person selling you property *actually owns it*. If that sounds simple and straight-forward, well… it isn't.

As a rule, most folks will not attempt to sell you something to which they have absolutely no claim whatsoever – the old Brooklyn Bridge scenario – but they may become forgetful of things such as their ex-spouse's interest in the land, or there may be tax or legal liens against the property of which they genuinely aren't aware. If you have a sharp eye, a lot of patience, and a thorough knowledge of land title law, you could examine the county record books yourself to see if there are any "clouds" or problems with the title, but most of us don't have that degree of diligence and expertise, so we need someone else to examine the title for us.

There are three ways in which you can approach this.

First, the old way: you hire your attorney to examine the title for you and advise you of any problems that he discovers.

If he makes any mistakes, that is, if he fails to notice something of consequence, he will explain the situation to you using lots of Latin phrases, and if you want to be compensated for your loss resulting from his negligence, you may choose to hire another attorney to sue him.

The modern way is to have your title examined by a title company which will detail any problems they find in the title, offer you a little help in curing them, then, when said problems have been corrected, sell you a policy of title insurance guaranteeing that you have good title. The price of this insurance is based on the sale value of the property, and so can cost from a few hundred dollars, to a few thousand for more expensive properties. This is the more prudent path to take.

And that, in essence, is everything you need to do to *safely* transfer property from one owner to another.

That's assuming that you're paying cash for the property, which almost no-one ever does, because land tends to cost a lot of money.

Since land does cost a lot of money, when a bank, or anyone else, loans you money to buy land, they'll want something to hold as collateral on the loan, and that collateral is most commonly the land itself. That is, they put a mortgage, or lien, on the property. This gives them the right to take it away from you if you don't pay them back. The bank's lien gets recorded at the courthouse along with the deed, and while recording a deed may be a fairly small item, today's mortgage instruments tend to run into ten or twenty pages and, depending on the fee charged by the Recorder, can amount to more than you'd pay for a fancy dinner out.

Along with the money you're borrowing, you'll get plenty of fully-justified intrusion into the process on the part of the bank. For example, you won't have to decide whether you want a title report or title insurance, because the bank will insist on the latter. They may also want to draw up all the papers, and they'll probably prefer to choose the title company to be used. If there are any improvements on the property, then they'll want to make certain that you keep these insured, and they may even require certain work be done on the improvements before they'll agree to make the loan.

There's no question that adding borrowed money to the picture complicates the purchasing process significantly. However, most folks then choose to add yet another layer of complexity, that of working through a real estate broker, also referred to as an agent. You may want to do this, or you may not, depending on the situation.

Typically, a real estate brokerage is headed by one or more individuals, holding real estate broker's licenses. These brokers are primarily responsible for the running of the business, and for the acts of their sales people, who must hold valid real estate salesmen's licenses.

(People often use the term "Realtor®" to describe any of these individuals, but that is not necessarily correct. The word Realtor® is a copyrighted term owned by the National Association of Realtors, which is the largest trade organization in North America, and one of the most powerful entities lobbying Washington, so only agents who are members of the NAR may legally use this term to describe themselves. For all their awesome power, nothing gets the NAR's collective shorts in a bind quicker than someone applying their name to a non-member, so don't do that. We won't use the term at all here, because we're going to refer to any broker, or salesperson as an "agent".)

Let's spend a few moments discussing the use of brokerages. I should tell you that in decades past, I worked as an active broker for about 15 years, and I held a valid Missouri Real Estate Broker's license for 27 years, so I have some familiarity with this business.

It is a common misconception that one is required by law to buy or sell real estate through an agent. Certain entities (see above) would like nothing better than for that to be the case, but it simply is not. That's not to say, however, that you might not choose to work with a brokerage in certain instances. In fact, it may be the only way to purchase a particular property on which the agent holds an "exclusive agency" listing.

Much has been written about the relative honesty of real estate agents, but I feel that the situation is best summed-up by this multiple-choice question/joke:

Complete the sentence: the real estate agent is working for_____.
The Seller
The Buyer.

The correct choice is C. Himself.

Historically, the agent has been employed by the seller, so legally, his allegiance is to the seller, but in any given transaction, the buyer is the one holding the money that powers the deal forward, so the smart agent will do everything possible to please the buyer if he wants to complete the sale and get paid.

And that, incidentally, is what the agent does best, bring the sale to fruition. Even if the buyer and seller become completely disgusted with one another – which isn't likely to happen because a canny agent will usually do everything in his power to keep them apart – the agent provides the impetus, as well as the contractual clout, to make the deal go through once a contract has been signed and money put into escrow.

At least that's the way it's supposed to happen. If you're unlucky, you may run into a situation where, for whatever reason, the agent would prefer another buyer (perhaps himself) over you. If that situation develops, you're not in a very good position. I'm sure someone representing the industry would be quick to point out that such behavior is disallowed by laws and rules of conduct, but such things are hard to see, harder to prove, and the real estate market is not a user-friendly place for the uninitiated. The prevailing climate is one where lots of money changes hands, and true professionalism frequently suffers.

If you're involved in a situation where you've decided to use an agent, then there are a few things that may be helpful for you to know. While commissions are not set by anyone other than the agent himself, most typically agency commissions tend to be 10% in rural areas and 6% in urban settings. Of this, the individual salesperson who lists and sells the property will probably be splitting his take with his broker, so they both get half. If another agency is involved, then the two agencies split the take 50-50 so that each broker and each salesman get 25% of the whole. It usually works like this: Frank Jones, salesman for Omnipotent Realty takes a listing on 40 acres in Polecat County. They place the listing in their files, and make it available to other agencies on the local MLS (Multiple Listing Service) so that any licensed agent who is also a member of the MLS can sell it. Later Joan Franks, saleswoman for Exaggerated Real Estate sells the property.

Let's say that the sale price is $100,000 so the seller pays a 10% total commission or $10,000. Each company will take $5,000, and each company will pay $2,500 to their company's salesperson. (This isn't always the way it works, but this is the most common split.) You should care about this, because to understand both the negotiations and the motivations of all the parties, you need to follow the money.

The way brokerages used to work, the seller would list his property with a broker, meaning that the two of them entered into a contract in which the broker/agent agreed to market the seller's real estate, so the brokerage in this case is the seller's agent. Then in the '70's, a new idea swept the industry, that of the "buyer's agent".

The way this works is that you, as a prospective buyer, sign an agreement in which you agree that you will engage this agent to work for you exclusively, and that you will buy property *only through this agent.*

There are a number of legitimate reasons why the agent wants this, as a hard-working agent will often spend quite a bit of time and money in the process of finding the right property for a buyer. And in fact, a good agent working with the protection of a buyer's-agent agreement will probably give you the most and best assistance in buying your land.

Unfortunately, as the buyer, you have little way of knowing whether the agent asking you to sign a contract is an especially good agent, or just a mediocre one.

Most of the arguments you hear for buyer's agency talk about how a good, professional, agent can be a major benefit to you and the negotiation process when he's not worried about losing your sale. I'm sure these anecdotal examples are all true, but I am equally confident that while there are indeed tens of thousands of top-notch agents out there, the fact remains that there are vast legions of amateurish, part-time, and otherwise unreliable, real estate agents lurking out there waiting to ruin what may seem like a sure thing. This is especially true during a boom market when it seems like every disgruntled waitress and disgusted truck driver in America decides to go into the real estate business.

When you wind up dealing with one of these individuals, you may find that the agent is going to try to sell you one of his own listings first, because he makes more money that way.

That's just human nature, and you don't have to sign an exclusivity contract with him for that. After "your" agent becomes convinced that he can't sell you any of his listings, then he'll start showing you listings of other agents and other companies, so your land-shopping experience is now filtered through what the agent wants you to see the most. If another agent is employed, you may not see all of the new agent's best properties, because he may have one or two listings that will be such easy sales that he's holding back to sell them to one of his own clients so he can make a full commission. Better that you call up each agent in your area to describe what you want instead of having "your" agent do it for you. You'll also get better information on the properties because you're one level closer to the actual seller.

Being closer to the seller is good, because he or she probably has the most accurate information about the property. Being closer to the seller can also be a bad thing though, if you and he don't hit it off too well. This is where the agent is most valuable: he can keep the deal moving forward to a successful closing even if one of the parties changes his mind. Be always aware that you may be that party.

Incidentally, I have read, from authors who have never worked in the real estate industry, that an ethical agent will never try to "steer" a sale as described above.

This is a hopelessly naïve attitude that ignores our truism about who the agent is ultimately working for (himself).

Besides that, it isn't even true; part of the agent's *job* is in attempting to steer the client. He will, for example, try to steer a client away from a property the loan for which he knows the client won't be able to qualify, or perhaps he'll try to steer the client away from properties that, in his opinion are over-priced.

He'll try to steer a client toward properties that he thinks will serve his client best, and he may also try to steer his clients toward situations that will make him the most money. If the agent is good at what he's doing, the client will feel "advised" rather than "steered". This is no more unethical than the buyer who wants to pay the lowest price possible, or the seller wants to receive the most money possible.

Most generally, an agent will also try to steer a client if he has what appears to be two qualified buyers for the same property. He'll try to parlay that situation from one sale into two by getting one party to prefer another property. He may do this at the risk of losing them both.

Please hold onto your hate-mail for just a moment longer, I'm not saying that signing an Exclusive Buyer Agency Agreement can't work for you, I'm just saying that you can do just as well for yourself, probably better, by doing your homework and shopping around with all agents *and* with private sellers. I'm also not saying that all real estate professionals are crooks. I *am* saying that there are bad apples in every industry, but getting ripped off buying a pair of shoes isn't quite so painful as having a land deal cost you tens of thousands of dollars unnecessarily.

Probably the most contentious part of a real estate deal is the aspect of information about the benefits and drawbacks of each individual property. The buyer always wants more information, or he should, but the more information the agent imparts, the more he risks having critical information prove to be incorrect. This is a very real concern for a scrupulous agent, because it's not uncommon for some sellers to play fast and loose with information that they pass on to the agent.

The agent has ways of avoiding liability for poor information. He may, for example, use phrases in his advertising like, "*seller reports* that this is a year-round spring." Some people assume that the seller will be the best source of honest information, because he or she is just an average citizen like oneself. The problem with that is that you don't need to keep a license to be an average citizen the way your agent has to maintain a certain level of honesty (or cover himself sufficiently) just to stay licensed to do business. The seller isn't so constrained, and may be living in on the other side of the earth when that spring goes dry.

Chapter 3: How to Buy Land Very Cheaply

Since this book is about land, the use and management thereof, you'll find it a lot more fun if you can play along by owning some land yourself, so that's what I've dedicated this chapter to: you being able to buy some land, even if you don't happen to be obscenely rich. (If you have disgustingly vast sums of cash, you may wish to skip to the next chapter.)

It seems as if everybody wants some land, and those that already have it want more. I suppose there are a few exceptions to this rule, but not many, because even a monk needs a monastery. That's why land prices are always high, and why some folks feel that if they can't afford to buy land now, they'll never be able to in the future.

Perhaps that's why tax sales and foreclosure auctions are so popular: the lure of getting something extremely valuable for a price we can actually afford. Alas, tax sales may be a dandy way for the state to collect its due, but the buyer frequently does not end up with marketable title, and in similar ways, foreclosures may prove to be far more trouble than they're worth. Both methods are even more complicated than they look, and while bargains do exist, so do many pitfalls await the uninitiated who haven't done due diligence. There's also the fact that you have no control over the location and type of property that becomes available for distress sales.

After a time, we get the idea that, if we only have a limited amount of money to spend, we need to accept land which is deficient in some way; property adjacent to a land-fill perhaps, or without deeded access, or with some other aspect that we wouldn't consider if we had other choices. We feel that we must pay some other cost in lieu of the cash we don't have to spend, in order to get an affordable deal.

Or at least that's what a lot of people think; it's the Hair-shirt Theory, but it's far from true. In fact, the best way to save hot, steaming piles of cash on a land purchase is simply to find someone whose plans have changed because, even in this day and age, unwanted land still exists for those who know how to find it.

Here's an example: Arlene met Bob at Woodstock. Together they planned to leave New Haven as soon as Arlene finished her degree in anthropology. They had an idea to move out into the country and let their lives regress to the Stone Age. They'd live nude except for animal skins, and make their living foraging for roots and berries. After a few years, they'd write a book and become famous. So, with some money from her inheritance, they bought forty acres of wooded land in the Midwest with a really charming cave, and began to fashion their future.

However, it turned out that Bob had uncouth personal habits, and Arlene was quite a bit of a nag. Thus, it came to be that Arlene and Bob gradually grew apart, and went their separate ways.

That was years ago, but Arlene still has that property. She hardly ever thinks about it though, except when the annual tax bills come in. Even then, the taxes on vacant woods seem so cheap compared to her Atlanta condominium that she just pays them without much thought. The price she and what's-his-name paid for the land back then wouldn't buy her a space in the parking lot today, so she doesn't view it as much of an asset.

I suppose you could say that Arlene's lust for land has been fairly sated by this time.

So you're thinking, "That's a great story Neil, and if I had the rest of the morning to waste, I'd sure like to hear the whole thing, but since I don't, and since I don't know anybody like you're describing in the area where I want to buy land…"

Bear with me a moment.

You can find people like Arlene *everywhere*. It's simple. But first, you'll need a couple of tools.

Tool Number One: A County Ownership Plat Book. Each county in every state makes their real estate ownership data available to private mapping companies who make maps detailing all the land ownership in the county. You can usually find these for sale in one or more of the offices in the county courthouse. They tend to run $25-80.

[BELOW] Here's a page from the appropriate county plat book showing the Arlene Doosis 40.

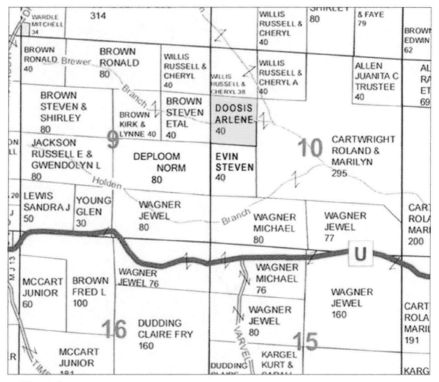

Figure 3

Tool Number Two – Maps: It would be a nice idea if you have plenty of maps of your area. I used to buy these on paper too, and I have a large collection of them, but now I find that I can get everything I need online and for free. As time goes by, my paper maps are growing outdated and while I still appreciate them for their aesthetic beauty (when applicable) their utilitarian value is diminished, although there are times when old maps can still offer insights into modern-day properties, as we'll see later in this chapter.

Let's take a moment to discuss a few types of maps that are particularly useful – and their limitations.

County Highway Maps: Most states offer county maps on the internet which have been prepared by their respective Departments of Transportation. Their primary benefit for our purpose is that, in addition to roads, towns and cities, many of them, particularly those from the more rural states, show the PLSS grid, so they make a nice place to start your search for any given property. If you have a legal description, but no ownership plat, see if you can find one of these to work with.

U.S.G.S. 7.5-minute Topography Maps: Accurate, beautiful and universally available, the paper versions of these maps have been the basic tool of the real estate industry throughout the last half of the 20th Century and the Adobe.pdf versions you'll find at http://www.store.usgs.gov remain so today. Unfortunately, I must qualify that statement: the accuracy of the paper maps was unparalleled, their only failing being that they were only updated infrequently. Most of the online versions currently available have been updated using automation that apparently makes wild, and very frequently incorrect, guesses. You can still rely on the contour lines, as those rely on the old data, but many of the updated roads are actually private driveways, abandoned trails, or simply some misguided computer's fever dreams. Even worse than this, not all states' maps show the PLSS grid, although as of this writing we're told that they all will someday. Luckily, many of the old *un*-updated maps are still available online, and of course there are the old paper versions.

Google Earth®: This is the answer to a dream we didn't even know we had. Google Earth® is aerial photography of the entire globe that allows you to zoom in and out and fly from one place to another. This is not to be confused with Google Maps®, Bing Maps® or Yahoo Maps®, all of which are nearly useless for our purposes here. You can use GE to measure property with amazing accuracy, then define boundaries with a drawing tool. You can work with a flat image showing land as viewed from straight overhead, or tilt the screen for a very realistic view of the terrain. Furthermore, it allows you to travel in time to see what a given property looked like in the past, going back to around 1995. GE is updated about every three years in most locations, and the resolution improves with successive generations.

Throughout this chapter, I've placed different views of Arlene Doosis' 40-acre parcel on several different maps, to give you an idea of how much you can learn about a particular property without ever leaving home.

[BELOW] This topography map tells us that the Doosis 40 has an elevation range of about 140 feet from the high-point on the northern boundary to the intermittent stream on the east side. However, it shows no sign of any access road.

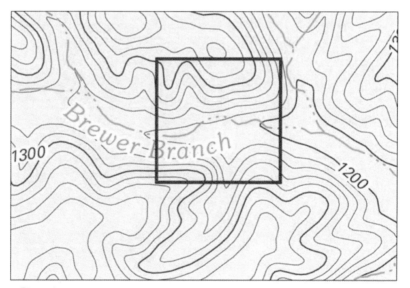

Figure 4

[BELOW] This time at least, the latest Google imagery isn't much help. We see that here's a road not far away, but no indication of how to access the property.

Figure 4a   © 2014 Google

[BELOW] This aerial view from 1995 sheds more light on the situation, literally, as the leafless trees allow us to see what appears to be an old trail coming in from the west. That's not to say that there's a legal easement, but it's a nice start. Plus we see a couple of what appear to be abandoned buildings that may hint at an old well or other improvements.

Figure 4b   USCS/Google

Tool Number Three - The County Assessor's Office

The last tool you need comes to you free with your real estate taxes. It's the County Assessor's Office, which keeps track of who owns what land in the county in order to assess property taxes.

That means that you can find the names of the owners of the blocks in your plat book there, as well as their addresses.

Oh, something I should probably have mentioned sooner: this method of Buying Land Very Cheaply is sure-fire and proven, but it does have a couple of drawbacks.

Drawback Number One: There's work involved.

Drawback Number Two: You'll still need some money to buy land. That's why this method works. All those other methods that don't involve you having money don't work – a big difference.

What you want from the County Assessor's Office are the names and address of all landowners in your area of interest who have out-of-area addresses; the further out-of-area the better.

Arrive at the assessor's office with a friendly smile, tell the clerk that you'd like to copy some addresses for property owners in Sections X and Y, and ask if she could show you to the appropriate book(s). (Later, you can ask for Sections Z and A if you don't get enough names. I don't recommend that you go in sounding as if you're going to be there all day.)

I also suggest you try to define your area to four or five mile-square sections. Using your topography map, pick the sections you're interested in, write down the number, township and range, and take that information to the assessor's office. (See Chapter 9: How to Read Legal Descriptions.)

Once you have the names and addresses of each out-of-area owner of vacant land in the area where you want to buy land, go back to your maps, and see how many of the properties appear to meet your broad criteria.

If your land needs are very specific, then you're going to be doing more work than if they're fairly general. For example, if you just *have* to have frontage on a stream, then you'll want to concentrate on locating streams as they cross properties in the plat book.

You'll be able to eliminate several of your choices using the maps, but when you get down to the most serious candidates, you'll want to go visit the properties in person.

When you do, be sure to take a topography map and compass with you, and be careful to avoid trespassing on neighboring properties, whose owners may be more close at hand than the owners of the properties you're looking at.

Once you've gathered your addresses and very thoroughly examined all the candidate properties, it's time to go back home and write a few letters.

To each of the out-of-area owners you've selected, you send a letter something like this:

Arlene Doosis
232433 Swansong Street, Apt 98
Atlanta GA 20144 Dear Ms. Doosis:

I am writing to inquire about your 40-acre property in Polecat County.

I am in the market for a property such as this, and I would be willing to pay you $[give your specific offer] for your land, should you be interested in selling.

If you would consider selling this land, please contact me at the address below. Sincerely,

You

Note that we don't dwell on formalities here. It's important that you make the deal very straightforward. Perhaps now you see the tricky part. You have to be sure enough of yourself and what you're willing to pay to put it up front.

I recommend that you send out as many as a couple of dozen of these letters, perhaps in groups of five or six.

When you start mailing them out and your replies start coming in, you will mostly get any of three sorts of responses: they'll either ignore your letter completely, accept your terms, or inform you emphatically that the property is worth much more than whatever you said you'd give, which you may treat as an offer to negotiate.

So are we taking advantage of someone here? Not at all.

Let's take a moment to talk about the concept of what land is worth:

Nobody knows.

That is, there is the profession of appraising real estate, and while that may be a noble and scientific profession, when they assign a price to a particular parcel, that does not mean that they will give the owner that much money for the land in question, only that similar sales in the area (if any) have suggested what the price *might* be.

In our exercise here, you are putting yourself in the position of a much more authoritative appraiser because you're backing up your appraisal with cash.

Cash has a lot of appeal to Arlene. Even though her land has value, if she wants to sell it, she needs either to list it with a real estate agent, or make the effort to sell it herself.

The majority of real estate agents prefer spending their time promoting larger, improved properties, which offer several times the commission, and probably for a lot less effort than marketing Arlene's remote forest. In a not-particularly-stellar market, her property could wait years for a buyer. If she has the wherewithal to advertise it herself, she'll need either computer savvy or money— both would be best — and a certain amount of time to devote to the effort.

If you send a letter such as described to a dozen people in the typical desperate-as-usual economy, at the very least, one or more of them is likely be going through some sort of personal crisis, and would much prefer to have some cash than a piece of land that sits unwanted and unloved, perhaps in another state. I will all but guarantee you that you will be doing something to help out another person in a very real way.

I once bought a piece of land from a dear old woman who just wanted the money to help her granddaughter with college tuition. She told me that the bus driver she'd talked to on her trip to the closing said, "I'll bet your land's worth a lot more than he's giving you" and she said, 'I'll take that bet, because I've owned it for thirty years and no-one's ever offered to give me *anything* for it.'"

There is no limit as to how low your offer can be, but it should be within reason, or it's likely to be rejected out of hand. The landowner only has to log on to the internet to compare your offer with what brokers are selling land for, so you can't be senselessly low, but since you're offering cash right now, a good many people will be willing to sell for significantly less in order to have a deal *right now* that doesn't include paying any commissions.

You can determine what is within reason to your own mind by simply perusing similar property on your state's Multi-list sites. Read forty want-ads and visit five or six of the properties, and you'll have about as good an idea of what that sort of land is worth as anyone else.

There's something else nice to know when you're thinking about how much to offer: many times the landowner's deed will specifically state how much he or she *paid* for the property. Knowing how much they stand to make (or lose) can help you in making your decision of   how much you want to pay. You can find a copy of the deed at the County Recorder's Office.

If that doesn't state the sale price, you may find an old mortgage on record that would give you some idea of the former price. Also, in some jurisdictions, revenue stamps are affixed to deeds in proportion to the sale price.

When you find a buyer who agrees to your price, you need to take charge of closing the transaction. You don't need an attorney here, just find a title company in the county seat. They'll examine the title for you, distribute the costs, and close the sale.

If you're going to give this method a try, I wish you good luck. I've purchased many parcels of land this way, and have without exception been given to understand that I was helping each of the sellers significantly, while at the same time getting a very good deal for myself.

There is little more that one can hope for in a transaction than when both sides walk away happy.

Chapter 4: Buying Land at a Tax Auction

Not So Fast

I'll bet that, if you're old enough to read, you've already seen a lifetime's supply of get- rich-quick ads with blazing headlines like *"How to Retire at 12 as a Land Baron"* or *"How I Became Obscenely Wealthy Buying Real Estate at Tax Sales"*. Perhaps you've wondered why, if making a fortune is all that easy, the authors of these books, brochures, and seminars had to resort to hawking their books, brochures, and seminars in the first place. When you hear, or more likely, read about, someone buying land "for the back taxes" it's a pretty good bet that there was, at the very best, quite a bit more involved in the transaction than that.

What I have to tell you won't do anything to dispel your cynicism. Just like so many other things in life, if it sounds too good to be true, then it probably is. That's not to say, however, that you can't obtain title to land through a process that *begins* with your successful bid at a tax auction, but it's far from a sure thing, and it probably isn't what you'd consider easy, and certainly not quick. On the other hand, you may find that tax auctions can provide a nice source of income, a way to own land without spending a great deal of money, or just a way to pick up that property that adjoins yours. If you do succeed in finally acquiring title, it will most likely be because you did your homework and understood the appropriate laws and customs.

Buying land, or a tax certificate, at a tax auction, is not something you want to do carelessly. For example, last year I bought a tax certificate on a small property that appealed to me, only to find when I got home, a one-word error in the legal description that the County Tax Collector had published in the paper.

Having the same sort of larcenous reactions as the next guy, my first thought was to cross my fingers and keep quiet, but if someone else had noticed the error in the future, the whole sale could have been thrown out anyway, perhaps after I'd added substantially to my investment by ordering title work and hiring an attorney to quiet the title.

Laws governing how delinquent-tax properties are sold vary from state to state, and whether you consider such sales to be an attractive deal for you will probably depend to a great extent, on where you live, because although there is a great similarity in how most jurisdictions go about these matters, there are also a few outliers where details are decidedly dissimilar.

Here's how it typically works: after a landowner has become delinquent in paying his taxes for a period of time, commonly two or three years, the collector will publish an advertisement in the local newspaper offering to sell tax certificates, or a tax deeds, on delinquent properties at auction. Before you begin in earnest, your first step should be to study your state laws relating to tax auctions. You can find most everything you'll need to know in a couple of web searches. You can also find information about where and when auctions are held in your county, or if you prefer dealing with humans, just call up the County Collector's Office at your local county seat. Tax auctions are held annually, usually on a date prescribed by state law, so the first thing you need to find out, is when your local auction will be held.

When that time comes, generally the month preceding the auction, the properties whose certificates are to be auctioned off will appear in the "Legals" section of a local newspaper, or better yet, you can stop by the Collector's Office for a copy of the list which may be updated with more recent information than the newspaper.

Viewed from the broadest perspective, tax sales are of two types: those that give the successful bidder a Collector's Deed to the property immediately after the sale, and those where the successful bidder is purchasing a Tax Certificate rather than a deed, which is given after the expiration of a redemption period. Some tax-deed states have redemption periods when the owner who failed to pay the taxes may recover the property following certain rules, some don't.

In either case, however, the most important thing for anyone anticipating buying land at a tax auction to remember is that a Collector's Deed does NOT grant clear title to the property, meaning that the title cannot be insured, thus making it impossible, or at best very unlikely, that the property can be sold or mortgaged. We'll get into how you go about getting marketable title to land you bought at tax auction in a bit, but for now, let's examine the two sorts of tax sales.

Tax Collector's Deed Auction

If you are of the habit of not paying your real estate taxes in a timely fashion, then it would be better for you not to be located in one of the states which sell delinquent properties via Collector's Deed auctions because in these jurisdictions, the process of losing your land is faster, less restricted, and more streamlined. That is, the delinquent owner has less opportunity to redeem what was formerly known as "his" property before it winds up in the hands of an auction bidder or claimed by the state.

At a Collector's Deed auction, you are presented with a deed either immediately after the auction, or after a brief redemption period. This gives you the opportunity to begin clearing the title to the property after a shorter period of due process. Since you are the owner of record (after your deed is recorded, of course) you can begin to use the property, although you shouldn't do very much work, or spend very much money, because you still don't have marketable title.

You absolutely should not move onto the property, or start to "clean things up" by removing anything you find there.

If your state is one of the ones listed in the accompanying chart as a Tax Deed state, you can skip the next topic and go directly to "Quiet-title Suits"

Tax Collector's Lien Certificate Auction

When you are buying only a tax lien certificate, you haven't actually bought the property, you've bought the right to pay the past due taxes.

Why would you want to do that? Two reasons: first, this is the only path available to get the property titled in your name, second, if the tax-delinquent owner surfaces and redeems the property, you get to charge him interest on the money you bid to win the auction, plus (maybe) some of the incidental expenses you will have incurred, such as having a title search done.

Whether the latter reason is sufficient reward for your costs depends on you and the laws in your state. Tax sales don't tend to draw the sorts of high bids you might see if they were simply auctioning off a parcel of land.

Some folks with plenty of free cash actually make a living buying tax certificates simply for the interest they gain, however, if you want to do this, you have to be prepared to wind up in ownership of the property, meaning that you'll have additional expense clearing the title and perhaps marketing the property. So to summarize that point, if you want to wind up owning the property, you may not, and if you don't want to wind up owning the property, you may.

If your state limits the amount of interest you can charge to a relatively low amount, then, if your winning bid is low, let's say $500, then you'll risk your time researching and bidding on the property, then waiting until the redemption period expires, for a relatively insignificant amount of gain. In Oklahoma, for example, winning with a $500 bid would cost you over two years of your time and net you $80 for your effort and investment in the event that the property is redeemed. It's easy to imagine that there aren't very many people trying to make a living buying tax certificates in Oklahoma. By contrast, in Connecticut you'll probably have to bid more, but you'll make over twice as much interest (18%) on the larger sum in half the time (1 year). Needless to say, the state you're bidding in makes a major difference. I'm assuming though, that your interest isn't in charging someone interest on a small sum of money, but in obtaining title to a piece of land to call your own. I'm about to tell you how to go about doing that.

Naturally, each state has its own particular process, but they're mostly pretty similar and go something like this: suppose you've found a property that interests you. The published notice will give you an abbreviated statement of the legal description and the amount of the taxes due. However, there are a lot of other things you're going to want to know before you're ready to bid on the property.

I'd strongly recommend that you find the physical location of the property and look it over. That, as you will quickly learn, isn't nearly as simple as it sounds. After you've read Chapter 10 and learned how to read the legal description, then you can probably get a pretty good idea of the approximate location of the tract you're interested in, but it's doubtful that you'll be able to see where the exact boundaries are.

Chapter 5 will give you a *little* help with this, but you may not be able to follow all those suggestions on a property you don't already own.

Through a process of thorough research, you may discover things that give you an advantage over other bidders. For example, this year, I plan to bid on a property that I owned and sold many years ago. I'm doing this largely because I know things about this property that most folks won't know. In the public notice, the property is simply described as 5 acres, but there's a lot more to it than that.

First of all, I know that the last owners of the property, an older couple, are both deceased, I also know, that the only heirs have absolutely no interest in the land because I've spoken with them. This presents a better prospect to me, because it means that if I win the bidding, the likelihood of anyone redeeming the property is slim to none. If I know something like this, I'm more likely to bid higher than someone who hasn't done his homework, and who's just looking to win a bid with a low price. In my neck of the woods, that describes most of the other bidders.

There's something else, however that I don't know: I don't know whether there's a mortgage or other lien on the place.

Now it's true that a tax deed trumps any previous liens or mortgages, that is, when you receive a tax deed to the property, not only has the previous owner been presumed to have forfeited his rights, but so have any lien-holders.

However, as part of your requirements for gaining title to the property, if you win the bidding, you'll need to spend a hundred and fifty, maybe two hundred dollars or more, on a title search showing whether there *are* any such holders of publicly-recorded deeds of trust, mortgages, leases, liens or claims. If this is the case, then it is your duty to notify these parties by certified mail, as well as the delinquent owners, so that they can redeem the property, i.e. pay the taxes and nullify your tax certificate, should they so desire. (Be sure to give the collector's office the paid receipt for the title search in order to be reimbursed in case the property is redeemed.) This is when you get to charge your whopping rate of interest.

What follows is a description of how the process proceeds from here in my state (Missouri). Things will probably be very similar in your state, but there will be differences, so pay close attention to any local instructions that the collector has to offer you.

If no-one redeems the property during the redemption period, which is most typically one to three years, then you must file an affidavit with the county collector stating that you have performed the requirements of the tax certificate, which entitles you to what the county may euphemistically call "clear title" to the property, that is, they will deed the property to you via a Collector's Deed or Tax Deed.

When requesting your Collector's Deed, you will need to have the following items:

- A copy of a recent Title Search Report.
- Receipts of all the certified mailings you have sent to previous owners and lien- holders.
- Copies of the First Class letters you sent to previous owners and lien-holders (copy the envelope).
- Copies of any letters sent to "Occupant" at the address of the subject property in case the certified letter is returned unsigned.
- Your Tax Certificate.

Show up with all these things, and that's all you need in order to get your Collector's Deed, making you the owner of record.

Well, that sounds nice and final, doesn't it?

Unfortunately it isn't.

Quiet-title Suits

Imagine that, for whatever reason, perhaps through no fault of your own (exactly) your property, or a lien certificate thereof, gets auctioned off at a tax auction, and you don't even find out about it until after the redemption period is over.

How would you feel? Well, stupid and mad are two good possibilities here. Then imagine what you'd do. My guess is that you'd hire an attorney and fight like a wounded grizzly to get your property back.

That's why, as a general rule, title insurance companies will not insure your title if it comes only via a Collector's Deed. One title examiner told me that their company might insure one after 27 years. I'm not sure what that number represents, but it gives you some insight into the matter of how much a Collector's Deed is worth.

However, waiting for the better part of three decades isn't really anything that very many people want to do, and there are numerous civic-minded reasons why it's better to bring things to a head well before that. So, in order to get the property back to where it earns the county income again, the legal community has created the Quiet-title Suit. As the petitioner in such a suit, it will be your burden to prove that the auction process followed all the proper steps; that everyone's name was spelled correctly; that the advertised legal description was correct; that all the appropriate mailings got mailed, and so forth.

Now is the time when you want to have carefully followed the process, checking and double-checking everything as you worked to obtain your Collector's Deed, or to rue your carelessness if you did not. If you were sloppy, or tried to cover up existing owners or liens that you knew about, this is also the time to look for a nice, soft spot where you can beat your head against the wall.

As mentioned earlier, a couple of years ago, I won the bidding on a small parcel, but then noticed that the Collector's Office had made a mistake in the legal description that they published. I could have kept quiet and risked more time and expense on the bet that no- one else would notice, but I felt better of it, and informed the Collector of her (boneheaded) error. I got my bid money back, and the property was rescheduled to sell at the next year's sale, so I'll try again then. Chances are, this might never have been noticed, but if it ever did come to light, it could result in the tax sale, and thus my title, being invalidated.

As part of the title-quieting process, your attorney will place an advertisement in a local newspaper. This ad, which is to run for several weeks, calls for anyone who thinks they have an interest in the property to appear at the quiet-title hearing.

You can do all this yourself without hiring an attorney, but don't. No matter how knowledgeable you may be of legal proceedings, the judge, you'll recall, is an attorney too, and most attorneys agree that any tightwad who acts as his own attorney deserves whatever he gets. The court will also appoint a guardian *ad litem* to represent the interests of infants, the unborn, incompetent persons and others who might have a claim to the property, as well as the ubiquitous John and Jane Doe.

Although jumping through all these hoops may seem like a challenge, in its essence, the quiet-title suit is setting up protection of your ownership of the property from the rest of the world as of the date of the suit, so don't knock it.

I live in a very rural, decidedly poor area, so you probably can't expect to get an attorney to handle your quiet-title suit for much less than the $1,000 or so that one costs me here, and if you live in a county that has more than five traffic-lights, be prepared to pay a good deal more. If you are fantastically wealthy and have a full-time attorney on your pay-roll, the quiet-title process can be completed perhaps in as little as five or six weeks, but if you are an average schmuck such as myself, I recommend you give it three or four months.

Finally, on the day of your court appearance, you stand before the judge, get sworn in, and your attorney asks you several questions about what has been done to find any errant owners or lien-holders of the property. You answer "yes" to all of his questions, and… that's it. The judge pens a judgment, you or your attorney record it, and viola!, after only two to four years, and after tolerating a lot of red tape, you've become the record owner of a piece of genuine Mother Earth; you've probably learned a few things, and if you enjoy amateur detective work, you may even begrudgingly admit that some of it was sort of fun. Sort of.

Toward that noble and illustrious end, here's a brief outline of the various states' basic rules regarding Tax Auctions. Enjoy.

State	Tax Deed/ Tax Certificate	Redemption period	Permissible interest rate
Alabama	Tax Certificate	3 years	12%
Alaska	Tax Deed	1 to 10 years	Not applicable
Arizona	Tax Certificate	3 years	16%
Arkansas	Tax Deed	30 days after sale	Not applicable
California	Tax Deed	Not applicable	Not applicable
Colorado	Tax Certificate	3 years	Fed. Dis. Rate +9%
Connecticut	Tax Deed	1 year	18%
Delaware	Tax Deed	60 days	15%
Florida	Tax Certificate	2 years	5% to 18%
Georgia	Tax Deed	1 year	20%
Hawaii	Tax Deed	1 year	12%
Iowa	Tax Certificate	2 years	20%
Idaho	Tax Deed	Not applicable	Not applicable
Illinois	Tax Certificate	3 years	18%
Indiana	Tax Certificate	1 year	10% to 15%
Kansas	Tax Deed	Not applicable	Not applicable
Kentucky	Tax Certificate	1 year	12%
Louisiana	Tax Deed	3 years	12% + 5% penalty
Maine	Tax Deed	Not applicable	Not applicable
Maryland	Tax Certificate	6 months	6% to 24%
Massachusetts	Tax Deed	6 months	16%
Michigan	Tax Deed	Not applicable	Not applicable
Minnesota	Tax Deed	Not applicable	Not applicable
Mississippi	Tax Certificate	2 years	18%
Missouri	Tax Certificate	1 year	9%
Montana	Tax Certificate	3 years	10% + 2% penalty
Nebraska	Tax Certificate	3 years	14%
Nevada	Tax Deed	Not applicable	Not applicable
New Hampshire	Tax Deed	Not applicable	Not applicable
New Jersey	Tax Certificate	2 years	18% + 2% to 6% penalty
New Mexico	Tax Deed	Not applicable	Not applicable
New York	Tax Deed*	Not applicable	Not applicable
North Carolina	Tax Deed	Not applicable	Not applicable
North Dakota	Tax Deed	Not applicable	Not applicable
Ohio	Varies with county		
Oklahoma	Tax Certificate	2 years	8%
Oregon	Tax Deed	Not applicable	Not applicable
Pennsylvania	Tax Deed	Not applicable	Not applicable
Rhode Island	Tax Deed	1 year	10% penalty +
South Carolina	Tax Certificate	1 year	3% to 12%
South Dakota	Tax Certificate	3 yrs city 4 yrs.rural	10%

Tennessee	Tax Deed	1 year	10%
Texas	Tax Deed	6 months to 2 years	25% penalty
Utah	Tax Deed	Not applicable	Not applicable
Vermont	Tax Certificate	1 year	12%
Virginia	Tax Deed	Not applicable	Not applicable
Washington	Tax Deed	Not applicable	Not applicable
West Virginia	Tax Certificate	18 months	12%
Wisconsin	Tax Deed	Not applicable	Not applicable
Wyoming	Tax Certificate	4 years	15% + 3% penalty

*New York City and Nassau County offer Tax Certificates

Chapter 5: How to "Survey" Your Own Land

Disclaimer: Warning! Danger! Peligro! If you are a licensed, professional land- surveyor, reading this chapter may be a threat to your health and well-being as it contains enough estimates, approximations and out-and-out guesses as to risk inducing headaches, vomiting and/or hypertension in individuals trained in the exacting science of civil engineering.

If, on the other hand, you are a typical small landowner, you may find that this information, if used judiciously, may give you the ability to measure your land and locate your boundaries to a vague, kinda-sorta accuracy without costing you one red cent.

The profession of land surveying is a challenging discipline requiring years of training, a thorough knowledge of complicated mathematics, and a careful and painstaking personality. This is as it should be, because it is no exaggeration to say that the ability to pin-point and measure areas on the face of the earth is at least as important as any other advanced skill mankind has developed. Sometimes a matter of only a few inches can determine whether extremely valuable assets such as water wells and other major improvements are located on one's property, or on that of a neighbor. For these reasons, obtaining an accurate survey of a parcel of land is usually neither cheap nor fast, and there is absolutely no substitute for a full survey of one's land done by a professional surveyor and recorded at the County Recorder's Office.

Many times though, a landowner may find himself in need of a quick guess; an educated estimate of where the precise boundaries of any given property lie. Over the years, I've learned a few techniques, and developed a few of my own, that allow me to make what I hope we could call an intelligent guess about property lines. I've always referred to this as "hafast surveying". You may want to use a more graceful term if you can think of one.

Practitioners must always remember that the goal of hafast surveying is the reasonable approximation. What professional surveying is to a Monet or a

Rembrandt, hafast surveying is to a grease-pencil sketch on a coffee-stained napkin. If you have a reasonably correct legal description of the subject property using the Public Land Survey System (PLSS) and a few simple tools, then you can get a very good idea of the approximate size and location of your rural property.

Here's what you'll need;
- A compass
- A calculator
- Maps and aerial photographs: everything pertinent that you can find.

First, let's suppose that you know where one corner of the property is, and you want to find the back line. Let's also say that your property is a rectangular twenty acres like the one in the first photo below. Such twenties as this are the m ost common form of twenty-acre parcel, usually described as ½ of a ¼ of a ¼ section. It will have a nominal size of 660 feet by 1320 feet. (If you're already getting confused, maybe you should first read Chapter 10, How to Read Legal Descriptions, which waltzes you through the basics of land description.)

[BELOW] This photo shows the 20 acres we want to locate. The arrow points to one corner that we're pretty sure of, which is where we'll begin our "survey".

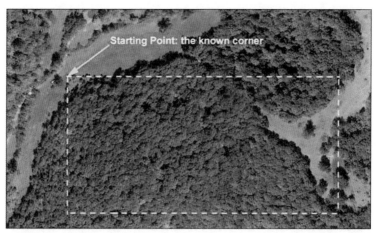

Figure 7   © 2014 Google

Since most properties in rural America are laid out using PLSS, the first thing we need to know is where the closest established line can be found. A pretty-good (a/k/a hafast) way to do this is by using aerial photography.

In days gone by, you could get aerial photos from the U.S. Conservation Service simply by paying an outlandish fee, and spending a few weeks following ridiculous governmental protocol.

Nowadays however, you can locate the same photos and better for free. (Free, that is, on your computer monitor, you still have to pay for hard copies.)

U.S.G.S topography maps are available at the U.S.G.S online store at www.store.usgs.gov, for sale on paper, or free in Adobe .pdf format.

[BELOW] See the patterns? Most of the single squares are 40-acre tracts that we can easily discern from this altitude. While one has to watch for jogs and extended sections using this technique, it's still a good way to confirm where boundary lines run in your neighborhood

Figure 8   USCS

In this instance (Figures 8 and 9) I chose to use older maps from the U.S. Conservation Service because like many of their black-and-white images, the one of the property I'm interested in was taken during the winter months, and it shows ground details like trails and roads that may be obscured by foliage in the summer months. (U.S.C.S. photos also tend to be older than Google Earth® images, and there are times when it's helpful to see what things might have been like a few years before.) Google Earth® also offers you historical images so that you can see aerials of the property of interest from several years ago. Often, the oldest of these images were taken by and for U.S. Conservation Service.

The first step in locating the property should be to step back (zoom out) and take a long view of the area. Unless the neighborhood is composed exclusively of very large parcels, we should be able to discern a grid-work of the PLSS system such as you see in Figure 7. (In this example, I had to go two or three miles from my subject property to find obvious property lines to follow, so the scale makes for some rather small images.)

[BELOW] This lower-altitude view shows the convergence of the lines that we drew on the higher-elevation view, confirming that the spot which we guessed was our corner is indeed so.

Figure 9   USCS

What I've done here is locate what are obviously accepted boundary lines in the general neighborhood that share common boundary lines with the property I'm interested in.

In Figures 7 and 8, I've found two of the boundaries of the parcel by this method, then I've marked them with blue lines. If you can find two perpendicular sides of a property, you're halfway home in confirming the location of the corner you want to start with. This step isn't always necessary if you've already got an idea of where one corner is, but it's nice to confirm that everything appears to be in order.

Next, I find the same corner in Google Earth® and, using the ruler function, which I've set to "path" I'll measure out the other two boundaries, and with that, I've got the boundary lines closed in.

[BELOW] Here's the corner we've located for our starting point. Looks like an old fence-row with trees growing in it.

Figure 10

base image © 2014 Google

Next, I look for landmarks on my photo which are clear enough that I can locate them both on the aerial photo and on the ground. It's preferable for these to be at the corner of the property if possible, so as to avoid further measuring, but if you can find something that's only along a boundary but not at a corner, you may be able to measure from there back to the corner.

In my example (Figure 9) I've found a line of trees that look like something we'll be able to recognize on the ground, but small enough to recognize as our corner when we arrive there in the real world.

Now it's time to hop in the truck and go out to the site. When you do, don't forget to print out copies of the maps and photos we're using and take them with you along with the compass and survey ribbon.

[BELOW] This is the pretty-obvious corner we saw in the previous photo where the cedar trees form a right-angle, although it's not so obvious here on the ground. We'll be traveling up the hill to the left of the photo from here.

Figure 11

photo: Neil Shelton

In Figure 11, we've arrived at the corner that we located on the aerial photo. We've found the trees we saw from the air, plus we were lucky enough to locate an old survey pin marking the corner (in this case, a piece of bent rebar), so we know we're (probably) in the right spot. This is a pretty obvious corner. We'll be traveling to the east (left side of the photo) from here.

The first thing to do is to mark the corner with a double ribbon on the nearest tree or shrub. Since I'm going to be going east from here, I make sure that the tail of the ribbon hangs down on the east side of the tree I'm tying it to, so that it will be visible for a long distance when I look back.

Now it's time to start measuring to the next corner, and when using the term "measuring", again, I'm being rather euphemistic. If we were real surveyors (at least in the pre- GPS days) we'd be getting out a long steel tape or chain for the measurements, as well as a chain-saw, lopping shears, and maybe a machete in order to clear a path. That would take a lot of time, it would amount to a lot of work, and would require at least two people.

Luckily though, we're just here to do a hafast job, so instead of taking an exact measurement, we're going to step off the distance

Frequently, when people pace off distances, they make long, exaggerated strides that they then count as three feet each. That, unfortunately, is just too hafast, even for us.

Instead, before we left home, we measured how many steps it takes us, while walking at our normal gait on level ground, to go 100 feet. We did this over and over until we were convinced that, using our particular set of legs, we covered 100 feet in exactly 39.5 steps. (Unless you are a midget or a giant, your steps will not be greatly dissimilar from this, but for better accuracy, measure for yourself.)

Armed with this home-grown knowledge, we deduced that our next corner, which is 1,320 feet from here, is only 521.4 steps to the east (13.2 x 39.5).

Now, if we were on open land, we might be able to see 1,320 feet in front of us, but unfortunately, this appears to be dense forest instead. So here's what we're going to set out to do: we're going to set our compass to sight due east to the first tree or other landmark that crosses our path, then we'll walk directly to that tree or landmark and tie a ribbon on it.

This is simple enough to describe (you did understand, right?) but it's a little more difficult to perform, even to our not-particularly-rigorous hafast standards.

First of all, I hope you'll be wearing boots because you really must not take your eyes off that tree or landmark regardless of what you're walking through, or upon whom you're stepping.

You also have to travel in as straight a path as possible. Drifting away from our line and/or taking our eyes off our tree can have disastrous results on our so-called accuracy because it is very hard to make certain that we have the same tree in your sights, even if we've only moved a few feet, or a few degrees from our original sighting. In fact, sometimes it can be very difficult if we take our eyes away, even if we haven't moved at all.

The other simple thing to do that's more difficult than it looks is sighting a straight line with a compass. I have experimented quite a lot with two different techniques: the first is to hold the compass about waist height, where you can read it, and where the needle stays relatively still. Then lift your chin up slowly to choose a landmark directly ahead.

The alternative, which I think seems as if it would be more likely to be accurate, is to hold the compass straight in one's direction of travel, then slowly bring it up to eye level, and sight along it as if it were a rifle.

Your results may vary, but to my surprise, I find the first method to be consistently more accurate.

When I arrive at my tree (or other landmark) I put a ribbon around it, leaving plenty of tail blowing in the breeze on the far side, that is, on the side in the direction that I'm traveling. Then I turn around and check with the compass to line up with my previous ribbon. If all looks good, I proceed to the other (far) side of the tree, sight again, and repeat the process.

Note that it is a little difficult to sight out a boundary and count your steps at the same time. You may want to sight the line first, then go back and measure it, or carry a note-pad and clipboard with you to log in the number of steps between each ribbon.

Okay, here we are at the second corner (Figures 12 and 13). We don't find any survey pin at all here, so we also search around the vicinity for a pile of stones, or one or two trees with two or three blaze marks on them. (Check out Appendix A at the end of this book for a list of common types of corner markers.)

What we find is a pile of stones that may have been used to mark the spot years ago… or not… but since it's close to what's left of some old fencing that seems to form a corner here, we figure we're in a pretty good location so we choose to move on to the next corner, resetting the compass to "north".

We follow the same procedure, except this time we have to travel 1/8 mile, or 660 feet, or 260.7 of our steps

Well, that wasn't quite as easy, but we did it. We've marked our tree, and we found an old fence half-buried in the leaves just a few yards away which is perpendicular to our path.

We evaluate this fence (taking care that the compass doesn't come too close to the wire) and determine that it runs fairly straight and due west.

After careful consideration, we've decided to choose this fence over the corner we set, based on the fact that the fence seems to have been fairly well constructed *at one time*, that is, it's straight and true. Besides, we generally give an existing fence preference over our own work because (a.) the neighbor probably considers it to be the line and (b.) we are, at risk of repeating ourselves, hafast surveyors.

Left: A barbed-wire fence that the tree has grown around. (You have to look pretty closely.)

Right: A pile of rocks, lest you had any doubts. Rural corner markings can be pretty nebulous. Prepare to do a little guessing. (This is an actual corner.)

Left: This is a remnant of an old wire fence. It runs straight and due west, so we'll treat it seriously as a likely boundary.

So now things get a little easier. We follow the fence, counting the steps and leaving a bit of ribbon on the fence at 100-foot intervals, just in case we may need to retrace our steps later. After a distance, we come into a clearing, and we can see our starting point from here.

Sighting to the tree where we began, we finally close the loop and we're done.

And there you have it. We've located our boundaries in such a manner that we have a credible idea where they are, and chances are we won't be antagonizing the neighbors with the results. Best of all, we haven't spent any money, in fact all it's cost us is a little blood from where we got caught up in the barbed wire, and what we've donated to the ticks we've picked up. (Hint: I find it's much better to pick ticks off at the end of the job rather than give them the chance to engorge themselves on the long, itchy drive back home.)

Real grown-up-type surveyors would most certainly want us to remember that the methods used here are not at all the fine and demanding techniques that constitute a Professional Land Survey, and should we be so foolish as to charge someone money for performing this service, they, or their trade association, will promptly sue our tick-infested pants off, in the event that they find out about it. Furthermore, if any of the boundaries we've just discovered are at all in question, or are in any way critical to the value of our land, we should not rely on them to be correct before we sell the property, the timber, or the minerals thereon.

Chapter 6: Building and Maintaining Roads

Without question, one of the very handiest things you can own when you live in a rural area is a four-wheel-drive truck. Your livestock, your income, even your health and safety can all depend on your ability to stay mobile in all weather, so having at least one four-wheel-drive vehicle can relieve you of a lot of unnecessary stress.

Having said that, you'll find that after a few weeks of enjoying your omnipotence over all sorts of terrain, you'll probably come to the conclusion that it is often nice *not* to need four- wheel-drive, especially for everyday events like trips to town, or short jaunts up to the highway to get your mail.

That's when you start to pay attention to the condition of your driveway and access roads.

When my wife and I first moved to this old farm, the only access to pavement was by two miles of county road. Actually, this wasn't so bad, since even though this road was rocky and full of pot-holes, the county was responsible for maintaining it, so it never really got *that* bad.

However, it never got any shorter either, and after a time, we began to eye an old log-trail through the back of our place which wound through some pretty formidable terrain, but which managed to access pavement in less than ¾ of a mile, since there is a state highway that adjoins our back boundary.

One day, when a much-too-small bulldozer became available to us, we reopened that crude, intermittent log trail and converted it into a crude *continuous* log trail that took us all the way from our back porch to the highway in less than half the distance we'd become accustomed to driving, with a fraction of the road dust, and without having to drive past the homes of any of our decidedly nosy neighbors.

We had those things during the very finest of weather, that is.

The trouble was, we did the road work in early fall, and the winter that followed did not offer us up the very finest weather on very many occasions.

The road wasn't so bad for the first quarter-mile, but then came a section where the old log trail had crossed the fence over onto the neighbor's property for a few hundred yards. There we had to blaze a new trail along the base of a hill that was perpendicular to the direction of the road. The resulting construction sloped decidedly to one side; the side with an old barbed-wire fence running very close to the track.

This was okay when it hadn't rained for several days, but when it was even slightly damp, the fresh, red clay that the bulldozer had exposed took on the texture and viscosity of axle grease. Attempting to pass this section with a two-wheel-drive was nothing short of madness.

With four-wheel-drive, the situation was actually worse, because now that we could *probably* get across this stretch without sliding sideways into the barbed-wire and over the edge of the embankment into the neighbor's field, so we had a tendency to take the chance.

[BELOW] An early horse-drawn road grader complete with operator and ballast.

Figure 15   wikimedia.commons.org

Remarkably, everyone lived through that period, which lasted for a few winters due to our perpetual lack of funds and our boundless, home-grown, naiveté. What I'd like to suggest to you is that you don't have to live with conditions like that. If you have home roadway problems, they probably can't be fixed for free, but they can be cured, or greatly alleviated, on a reasonably modest budget.

Let's start out with the very basics: suppose you have a stretch of woods through which you want access. In most forests, if you look very carefully, you'll be able to find some trace of old logging trails through-out the property. Look along ridge-tops and at the highest points of any given location, and you may see the slight indentations of old wheel tracks, or simply long stretches where a cleared arbor through the woods can be seen. Loggers tend to put their trails in places where water will run away from either side, which is where you'll want your road to be also. If you're lucky enough to find a trail that, sometime in the past, has been used quite a lot, there may still be an obvious path, even to the untrained eye. Wherever this is the case, you can have a passable trail in a few afternoons with just a little chain-saw work.

It's unlikely, though, that your old trail will follow the exact path that you want to use for your modern ingress and egress, so you'll probably have at least a few yards that will need to be cleared through existing forest.

This is where lots of people make their first big mistake: they cut all the trees and brush out of the new roadway, figuring that if they cut the stumps low enough, they can tolerate them until they rot out naturally.

I'm not certain how long it takes a few dozen stumps to rot away, because I followed this plan on one of my trails about 25 years ago, and most of my stumps appear as strong and sound as they were back then, so, just to be sure, allow yourself 50 or 75 years, especially for the more rot-resistant species like cedar, cypress and locust.

While I was making this mistake, I also made the companion error of thinking that I could have these stumps bulldozed out later when I had more money.

This brings us to:

Road-building Rule Number 1: You cannot push out stumps with a bulldozer.

Well, not unless you are dealing with some very small stumps *and* a very large bulldozer. Bulldozers are able to push down large trees easily because of the leverage they get by pushing on a point eight or ten feet up on the trunk.

However, stumps, by definition, have no trunks, and no trunk equals no leverage. So, after you've cut down the tree, the only practical way to remove the stump is to dig it out.

Basically, there are three ways to do this: 1. You can dig them out with a bulldozer, but this is very expensive. A typical stump can take a quarter to half an hour to remove. 2. You can dig them out with a backhoe. This is somewhat less expensive, but not cheap. The third way is to dig them out by hand.

At least I *assume* that's the third way, I don't know for certain, because I am not personally acquainted with anyone who has had the combination of ambition and free time that would be required to dig out a few dozen (or a few hundred) stumps set in rocky ground. I guess if one were a Pharaoh or monarch, one could produce that sort of man-power, but these days, even Pharaohs use heavy equipment. If you have a farm tractor, you may be able to pull out the very tiniest stumps yourself, but you probably won't have only tiny stumps, so this probably isn't worth the fuel you'll expend.

Rather, my advice is that if you have trees larger than 2-3" in diameter to clear from a roadway, you'll need to hire equipment. Most typically, this is done with a bulldozer, but in my experience, the best machine for removing the most trees in the least amount of time is a track- loader. For those innocent of construction machinery, a track-loader is virtually the same as a bulldozer, but instead of a blade in front, it has a bucket that can be lifted up high on the tree to achieve much greater leverage. This will probably cost you anywhere from $50 to $100 per hour, at least in rural backwoods areas like mine. If you have less than 1/8-mile of roadway to clear, the most important part may be whether or not your machine operator insists on a minimum time for the job. Most will want at least four hours (half a day's) work before they'll go to the effort to move their equipment to your site, and a full day minimum is more likely.

There are also places where you can rent the machine and operate it yourself, but from what I've seen, folks tend to shy away from letting strangers climb aboard hundred-thousand dollar machines to have their way with them. I know that the local Caterpillar dealer will do so, but you have to pay about as much as you would pay to get the operator, and the minimum rental is by the week, so this probably isn't a viable option.

After you get rid of the trees, you'll have a lumpy trail that a four-wheel-drive can pass over immediately, and after a few months of use, you might even be able to get a regular car over it in dry weather.

Wet weather is quite another story. Water is the ruination of roadways, and the sooner you're able to deal with the seasonal precipitation in your area, the sooner your road will go from a trail to a driveway. This brings us to…

Road-building Rule Number 2: Get all rainwater off your road as quickly as possible.

Obviously, the only practical way to do this is with crowning and ditching. You may have some spots where water can be drained from large pools with a pick and shovel, at least temporarily, but if you're trying to make a road that your in-laws will want to drive down in their Buick, you're going to need heavy equipment again.

Naturally, the equipment that does best at pushing out trees isn't going to do such an efficient job of digging ditches. That's how life works. In most cases, the best way to dig ditches is either with a road grader or a small bulldozer equipped with a six-way blade. These are not necessarily more expensive than large bulldozers or track loaders, but they are harder to find, and of course you have the daily minimum problem again.

Remember that the object is to get all the water off the road as quickly, that is, in as short a distance, as possible, so that it doesn't become a stream which will quickly cut a ditch of its own. That's why it's a good idea to have the roadbed "crowned" while the ditching is being done. This means that you make the center of the road a few inches higher than the sides, encouraging the water to flow into the ditches. If your road runs along the top of a ridge, you may be able to avoid any ditching at all in some areas, but when you start to move up or down- hill, or across saddles, ditches will become a necessity.

Now you've finally got a usable road that doesn't turn to soup every time it rains. You have a few soft spots that may *start* to improve during the dry months, never completely going away, but still, you can drive your road every day in all weather and, if you don't have any really steep hills, you may be able to get some delivery people to bring what you need right to the house (especially if they're selling you something).

But suppose you want to go at bit further than that. You want a smooth, trouble-free road that you can travel in second or third gear all the time. You want something UPS and FedEx aren't afraid of, and if you have garbage pick-up in your area, something the garbage truck can navigate without getting stuck, spending the afternoon there, and canceling your service. Which brings us to…

Road-building Rule Number 3: there is NO substitute for crushed rock.

The very best way to stabilize and smooth a new road is by applying crushed rock. If this sounds expensive, it can be. If you have a brand-new road, the road-bed will be very soft and you may need a LOT of rock, maybe ten or twelve truckloads per quarter-mile. On the other hand, if you've been driving your road for more than a year or two, then you may be able to get by with as little as a truckload per five hundred feet or so.

The purpose of the rock is to stabilize the surface. If you have soft spots that turn into a gooey bog after each rain, this is cured by rock. For the rest of the road, a thin layer of rock will smooth out the inconsistencies, harden the surface, and create the smoothest road you'll find short of paving.

Rock doesn't have to cost so much, but it can. In our area, you can get a large tandem- axle dump truck full of rock delivered for about $225-$250 (2014 prices). You may have someone suggest that you can save money by using creek gravel as it comes out of the stream- bed, which is called "creek-run" or screened creek gravel of whatever size you want (typically 1- inch). This tends to cost about half or three-quarters as much as quarried, crushed rock, but it has some drawbacks. For filling that giant mud-hole that swallowed the mail-man last week, creek-run will work pretty well, and is probably the most cost-effective way to go, but for long, thin applications, it doesn't do such a good job because whereas the angular, broken edges of the crushed rock dig in and hold themselves in place, the rounded creek rock tends to roll off into the ditch over time.

(Before mining your own creek rock, you should make certain that the stream where you propose to get the gravel is not protected by the Environmental Protection Agency.)

When ordering crushed rock, there are two types you need to be familiar with. The first, "clean rock", sometimes called "road rock" is simply rock of a given size only. This provides a uniform surface that can be graded and re-graded many times. It's a good way to dry up wet areas.

The second type is called "base rock". This is the most useful for all-around applications. Base rock is rock of a given size, plus everything else smaller than that down to dust-size particles. Base rock is about as close as most mortal beings will ever get to having a paved roadway. Once applied and packed down, it tends to hold its shape, and *it sheds water*. This last property is invaluable to your purposes.

1-1/2 to 2-inch crushed rock makes good material to fill deep mud-holes and long gooey ruts, plus it does a better, more stable job than creek-run. Apply 1-inch base rock over this 2- inch rock, and you'll bring your road surface to a wonderfully smooth condition that will be very, very apparent the first time you drive over it.

Crossing Water

As long as your crowned road passes over high ground so that water runs off and away from the road, then you'll soon have a firm road-bed causing you few problems, but unless you have a very short road, or live in a very flat area, you probably won't go far before you come to a water crossing, be it simply a hollow in which a wet-weather stream develops when it rains, or a year-round stream that you'll need to ford on a daily basis.

In nearly all such cases, you'll find that the simplest solution is usually the best.

[BELOW] Pouring crushed rock.

Figure 16   photo: Neil Shelton

In most cases, the simplest solution is what's called "armoring", that is, covering the part of the roadbed that crosses the stream or gully with a larger crushed rock known as "jaw rock", which will be a uniform size of 3 or 4 inches. It stabilizes the crossing area and may last for years, or only until the next really heavy rain, depending on how much water passes through under the wettest conditions. Armoring works pretty well, and only costs as much as a truckload of rock; it's a technique that you may choose in lieu of culverts or concrete if the stream isn't too large.

Culverts

Call them culverts, tin-horns, tubes, or whistles, a pipe that channels water under the road can, if properly installed, be a long-term, low-maintenance solution to your water problem, or if improperly installed - and plenty of them are - a constant irritation that you may eventually choose to replace. Unfortunately, in cases of private parties installing their own culverts, improper installation is the norm.

Culverts come in three types, concrete, steel or plastic. Concrete is, of course, the best, as it will last practically forever, so naturally it costs more - a lot more - to buy, to move, and to install. So much so, that you'll probably choose steel or plastic. Steel culverts are the old standby; their drawbacks are that they are heavier than plastic and can rust through in just a couple of decades in a moist climate. Since plastic culverts are priced comparably to steel, and since it's generally considered that their advantages outweigh their faults, plastic seems to be the coming trend. They're light, corrosion-resistant and if you hit an exposed end with a bush-hog, the results are less exciting than when rapidly whirling blades meet with corrugated steel. The main drawback is that they can catch fire from grass and forest fires, and if one end gets started burning, a chimney effect is created which will burn out the whole culvert.

A word of caution here: always use only double-walled plastic culverts with a smooth inside bore. The single-wall versions simply aren't strong enough for use as road culverts. That's why they're cheaper.

In order for a culvert to work successfully, several rules have to be observed during installation. First, the culvert needs to be installed below grade, that means that a trench must be dug not only deep enough to accommodate the size of culvert being used, but also at least three or four inches of gravel above it. If the culvert creates a noticeable rise in the roadway then this hump will eventually be pared down by grading, perhaps so much that the bare pipe is exposed, which will lead to its eventual deterioration, and besides, we don't want to purposefully ad another bump to the road if we don't have to. Second, the culvert pipe you choose must be of sufficient size to carry all the water that comes down the stream without overtopping. If flooding covers the entrance (upstream side) of the pipe, your culvert will quickly fill with debris, mostly rock, and to date there is no satisfactory way to clean out a 20-foot pipe full of loose stone without destroying it. Civil Engineers have fancy graphs and calculations to estimate how large a culvert needs to be in any given situation, but even those are no guarantee that the biggest rain of the millennium won't occur right after you install your new culvert, so the best way for undisciplined folks like you and I is to observe the stream-bed before the culvert is placed, then buy a pipe that looks to be large enough to contain all the volume that the stream banks will hold.

You can get an idea of how much water a particular stream-bed has seen by looking for packed leaves or other debris that previous heavy rains have deposited. Generally speaking though, if a stream flows constantly at your site, then you'll have a lot less grief over the years if you choose a solution other than a culvert, unless you are prepared to install a very large pipe.

You also shouldn't scrimp on the length of the culvert. Culverts can be had in any size you desire, but typically supply companies stock-pile them in ten- and twenty-foot lengths. Ten feet is enough to drive a car or truck over, but to avoid having people drive off the edge, thus collapsing the end of the pipe, to say nothing of what it does to your vehicle, always choose the twenty-foot length. It won't seem nearly so big once it's in the ground.

Maintaining Your Road

Once you've got a civilized road that allows you to travel in second or third gear, you only need a few things to maintain it.

Even if you've covered the entire road with crushed rock, you'll want to add more as needed in 5 or 10 years depending on your soil and weather conditions. Rock doesn't wear out of course, but it sinks deeper into the soil with use, and some of your smaller rock will wash off the roadway with each heavy rain.

You could decide that you're going to completely renew all the road rock every decade or so, but a better way is to add rock as it's needed each year to keep potholes and ruts from developing. Besides following the sensible path of only fixing what is broken, you'll only need gravel where it's obviously most needed. Following a conservative plan like this, you can keep the road in top shape forever without spending all that much money.

Equipment

Luckily, rock and fuel for the tractor are about the only on-going expenses you'll have. Then if you have one or two blades to fit your tractor, those should last you a lifetime. Let's talk about these blades:

The Straight Blade

Straight blades, both new and used, are quite common on the market. They range from small 48" Category-1 blades with manual angle settings up to 10 and 12-foot monsters with hydraulically-controlled angle, tilt and side-shift.

Your best bet for the money is to get a straight blade with manual settings for angle and tilt as shown in Figure 17. Those with tilt setting typically cost only a bit more than the simple angle-only models, and they provide you with the power to cut and clean ditches much more effectively, and to grade, by pulling material out of one ditch and spreading it across the road to he other side, the way full-size road graders do.

If your road doesn't have any added rock, or not much, then you'd probably get by about as well with only the straight blade. On the other hand, if you have a good covering of rock, then if you only have one blade, make it a box blade.

[BELOW:] A straight blade with manual angle and tilt.

Figure 17

photo: Neil Shelton

The Box Blade

The basic difference between the two is that a box blade does not angle or tilt and has closed ends that keep the material from falling away to the sides. The box blade will pick up a full load of rock, spread and level it, and keep as much material as possible right in the roadbed where you need it, but you lose the ability to cut ditches, or move material across the roadbed from one side to the other.

You can make and maintain big improvements to your road with either blade, but for the best job, you really ought to have both, unless you have a large budget, in which case choose a hydraulically-operated blade with removable end panels. These will do all the jobs that both the straight and box blades can do without your ever having to leave the seat of the tractor. You can buy new straight or box blades for a few hundred dollars each, or opt for the hydraulically-operated version for a few thousand.

My 3/4 mile driveway has become more than just an access route to me, it's become a source of pride. Maintaining it has become one of my hobbies. Sometimes I just sit and look at it with a moronic grin on my face. If you're not getting this kind of warm, fuzzy feeling over your access road, maybe it's time you did.

Chapter 7: Clearing Land

Once you've purchased your future homestead, especially through the methods proposed in this book, you're very likely to have bought a property that's been neglected or abused for several years. Of the two, neglected is far superior to abused. I hope you haven't bought a tract of land that's been recently timbered. Practically speaking, there's not a great deal you can do for such land that doesn't involve hours upon costly hours of heavy equipment work, or back-breaking toil for perhaps the rest of your life unless you're young and very energetic, and maybe even then. A clear-cut deciduous forest can take decades, generations in fact, to recover into anything approaching its original state. Should you decide to turn it into tillable ground instead, you'll have several hundred stumps per acre to remove, because waiting for them to rot out is, again, a matter of decades. As it is now, you can turn the ground into a sort of crude pasture, with sparse grass growing amid the stumps and brush, but it won't be anything that can be easily bush-hogged, let alone mowed, any time soon, so you'll need to keep it from growing up in brush by hand.

Neglected land is another story. If you have old fields that have gone to brush, and that brush isn't much larger than 2 or 3 inches in stump diameter, you can clear it with a bush-hog or tree-shear in a comparatively short time (hours or days). You'll still have stumps to deal with, but they will obviously be smaller and less of a challenge to eliminate or neutralize.

If you have mature forest, the prospect of removing mature trees may be daunting, but it's a job that many folks before you have completed and lived to tell the tale.

Remember though, that land clearing is serious business. The trees you are about to remove may well be a century or two old, especially if they're growing in less than ideal conditions. (Trees growing in extremely poor, dry, or wet conditions grow more slowly.) Once the clearing is done, your land will need consistent annual effort to keep it from growing up in brush and weeds. If you don't plan well, both for getting the clearing done, and for keeping the land clear, then you risk losing your valuable time, your sizable investment, and of course your century-old forest. Think it over before you clear.

Stripped to the essentials, there are two ways to clear land: by hand or by machine. That's if you've never done much clearing by hand. If you have, then you may very well feel that the only way is by machine. Some people will suggest a third method: goats, but I'd warn you that this route is much more popular among those who haven't tried it yet. Goats aren't going to eliminate anything much over four or five feet high, and despite what you may have seen in the comics, they can be rather finicky eaters if they don't happen to cotton to what you want to get rid of. Goats are a pretty good solution for *keeping* cleared land cleared, but not for clearing it in the first place.

If you've only got a tiny patch of ground to clear, and it doesn't matter how long it takes, then by all means do it by hand. You'll save quite a bit of money, get a quite a lot of exercise, and you'll also be treating yourself to quite an education in the process. If you actually ever get finished, you probably will choose to hire equipment next time - if there ever is a next time.

Of course, it's up to each person to decide how big a piece of ground has to be before it's considered more than a tiny patch. If you're thinking that clearing land only means going out with a chain-saw and cutting down several trees (which is plenty of work in itself) then you'll be getting the full helping of acquired education.

[BELOW:] Clearing land with a track-loader

Figure 18   photo: Neil Shelton

Personally, my acquired education on the subject tells me that the only amount of land where clearing by hand is worth the time and effort is in situations where machinery would not have *room* to work without damaging buildings or other desirable trees and plants in the process. In other words, pretty small places indeed.

Using machinery, you can go from dense forest to pasture or garden soil, in about two years time.

Getting Rid of the Trees:

Your biggest single expense will probably be what you spend to take the trees down. In the case of small acreages with small timber to be cleared, it may be that you would save money by hiring one of the smaller bulldozers the size of the Caterpillar D3 or the John Deere 450 but if you have over a couple of acres of mature trees to be removed, bigger is almost always better.

There are three machines you can engage to remove grown trees:

Bulldozer   Track Loader   Excavator

Of the three, there are more bulldozers available for hire in most areas than the other two. Track loaders, if you can find one, are probably the most cost-effective because they can push from higher on the tree, thus gaining quite a bit of leverage. Excavators can get very high leverage, and are the most efficient at burying the results, but still slower than the track loader, which makes the best all-around clearing machine.

If the timber you're clearing is predominately made up of valuable species like white oak, walnut, red oak, or hickory, and these are straight and tall enough to yield at least one 8-foot log per tree, then you should locate someone to buy the logs. You may not make a lot of money, but what you get will help defray the other costs, and the wood will go to some useful purpose.

Plus, you'll have a lot less material to dispose of afterward, which is no minor consideration. If this is what you want to do, you'll want to have your operator push all the trees over so the loggers can cut them up on the ground. This is really critical, because even very large dozers or loaders cannot get the leverage to push out mature tree stumps, so if the loggers come first, and fell all the trees leaving stumps in the ground, they'll have to be dug out, which is very, very time consuming, as already discussed.

How many hours of machine time your clearing job will take depends on a lot of variables including the size of the timber, the slope of the terrain, and the rockiness of the ground, but you should probably count on it taking approximately twice as long as you expect.

[BELOW] A tree-shear mounted on a skid-steer loader

Figure 19   photo: Neil Shelton

Operators of these tend to charge half or one-third as much per hour as the larger machines will cost, and in some cases they can save you quite a lot of money. They also save somewhat on topsoil loss, however, operators promoting tree shears tend to exaggerate the amount of topsoil loss that bulldozing causes. If the ground is immediately replanted so that there isn't a great deal of erosion, bulldozing doesn't destroy the topsoil so much as it moves it around a bit.

A tree-shear can cut off trees of up to 8 or 10 inches or so in diameter, depending on the species of tree and model of machine. Since the tree-shear clips the trees off about flush with the ground instead of pushing out the roots, you need to remember that these stumps will sucker back until you find a way to kill them, such as repeated bush-hogging or application of herbicides.

If you're clearing the land for pasture, after tree-shearing you can now keep it cleared either with a bush-hog or maybe even goats, but if you're looking for soil to garden or farm, tree-shearing just isn't the solution you need because of the roots left behind.

Getting Rid of the Trash:

In the past, when land has been cheap and money in short supply, the slash and stumps were just pushed up into a pile and left there for the ages (stuff like this takes a *very* long time to completely decompose). You can do this too, but unless you value the piles as wildlife habitat, it's better to get rid of the brush for a number of obvious reasons. The best way to do this, assuming you don't have access to some pretty large and expensive equipment like a smoke-less combustor, or a large tub grinder, is to burn everything you can and bury the rest.

Needless to say, burning has its risks. Not only do brush piles of mature trees make a very hot fire (for a few hours) but they can smolder and hold hot coals for over a week. Never forget that a supposedly dead fire that looks like only so much burned coal and ashes can spread far and fast if a wind comes up. In other words, you need to be prepared to keep close tabs on your fire, perhaps for five to ten days and not completely dismiss its potential danger until you can run your bare hand through the ashes.

I like to keep a few gallons of water close at hand all the time that I have a fire going, and either a back-pack sprayer or a gardener's watering can for application. You should alert the local fire or conservation department to the fact that you'll be burning, and have their number on your speed-dial until the fire is long dead.

While it is not completely impossible to burn tree stumps, it is very difficult due to their thickness and the fact that they generally have a good deal of soil clinging to the roots. Most people prefer to cut them from the trunk of the tree after it's been felled, then bury them – again, with equipment. Alternatively, you can haul them to be dumped somewhere else, where they can be put to some good uses, such as providing fish habitat at the bottom of your pond, or as erosion control in bare hollows and ditches. I've even seen rather attractive fences made from tree stumps — less the dirt in the root ball — lined up so that the roots make a barrier to traffic. Of course, if you can get the dirt out the root ball, you might as well burn them.

Preparing a Seedbed:

After your bulldozing is completed and the brush piles burned, what's left isn't very pretty. If you had large trees pushed out, then you'll have lots of rocks, roots and ditches, as well as gaping holes that can swallow a large tractor-wheel whole. Since you're presumably going to be using this ground for a long, long while, you need to smooth out the high and low-spots, pick up the rocks, and remove or kill all the roots that can turn into brush in a short time.

People with plenty of resources generally use a road grader or six-way dozer to do this job, but if you have the use of a farm tractor (the bigger the better, but most any size will do) you can pile or windrow the rocks and roots with a trash rake. A straight blade or box blade will probably come in handy for smoothing as well.

To complete the seedbed, you'll want to smooth and till your future field with a disk harrow. When you've done this, you should have a reasonably smooth bed without too many rocks, ready to accept your seed.

Seeding the Pasture:

You may be thinking that, if you're not clearing the land for pasture, then you can just stop there, but remember that whatever your intentions for your land, you need some plan to prevent erosion

At this stage, most ranchers will seed the area with a cover crop, something like winter wheat or rye that will grow up over the fall and winter, to be disked under for "green manure" in the spring. This is a good policy because it further pulverizes the seedbed and adds organic content to the soil as well as limiting erosion. If you need to add lime to the soil, this is also the time for that.

At last, it's time to seed your pasture.

As with so many things these days, this is a subject that is fraught with controversy. That's because of Tall Fescue (*Festuca arundinacea*). Tall Fescue is by far the most popular pasture grass in all areas of the United States where it grows well, that is, most of the eastern United States. In fact, there are 40 million acres of American grassland devoted to Tall Fescue.

Fescue grows well on a wide variety of soils and persists despite low pH and poor fertility. Individual plants grow as a bunch grass, but aggressive self-seeding quickly results in dense sod. These traits make fescue an attractive choice for lawn, pasture or erosion control plantings, even for homesteaders, but fescue is also especially prized by landowners for its ability to bounce-back after drought or heavy grazing.

Unfortunately, there are some problems associated with fescue; problems with foaling mares in particular, and with "fescue toxicosis" in grazing animals. Further, fescue grows so well in so many different soils that it is considered "invasive".

We'll not spend too much time on the controversy here, but as to whether to plant fescue or not. You shouldn't decide one way or another until you've thoroughly investigated both the advantages and disadvantages of fescue for your individual situation.

Cleared, and Seeded, and Keeping it That Way:

Finally, you've bulldozed your trees, burned the slash, tilled and seeded the ground. Now the long-term work begins.

Plan on bush-hogging or mowing your field at least once every two years, and annually is best, lest it starts to revert to forest. You may also want to consider "selective" herbicides that kill broadleaf plants (i.e. weeds) but ignore or even encourage grass to grow. Of the two, bush- hogging is by far the cheaper method, not to mention being a lot more ecologically friendly, and far more predictable. It's also better for your soil because the mulched debris you leave behind decomposes and adds organic matter.

Chapter 8: Drilling a Well

When Thomas Jefferson built his personal manse, Monticello, it was, compared to other architecture of the time, extraordinary, and not always in a good way. One of the most startling aspects was that it was built on a hill-top. That may seem commonplace today, but it was quite *avant garde* in the late 1700's, and not without good reason: building on a high knob meant an all-weather road was needed to get to the top, and of course many of Jefferson's multitude of agricultural pursuits had to be carried out on dry, rocky ground. Most troubling of all, Jefferson had to dig several wells, each deeper than the one before, and still they reportedly went dry one year in five, when water had to be hauled in to keep the household functioning.

That anecdote tells us something about the improvements in modern well-drilling equipment, and also quite a bit about the importance of having a reliable well. Jefferson pulled this off, of course, but he had slaves. Modern day landowners have to find other ways to get things done.

It is extremely unlikely that you will find anything that you can do to improve your parcel of land which will prove to be more valuable over the years than drilling a modern, deep, water- well.

Potable water is a basic requirement of life on Earth. Early man considered it a prehistoric no-brainer that the best cave or wig-wam site was one situated near a flowing stream or spring. Then, during the Neolithic Era, as nomadic lifestyles turned to agrarian, man learned that if he found a muddy area in the ground, he could dig it out, and the resulting cavity would fill up with water. Thus what your great-grandfather called a "spring-box" was the first shallow well. Deeper wells were lined, or "cased" with stone, wood, or even wicker to keep the walls from collapsing.

Hand-dug wells are still in use all over the world today, and you can sometimes find them in rural or forested areas of the U.S. They have one advantage, and that is that they are very inexpensive, depending on the value of labor. All that's required is a shovel, or if you're a true minimalist, a sharp stick, and you can dig one for yourself. Bear in mind though, that hand-dug wells also have many disadvantages, chief among which are the obvious lack of sanitation and the poor reliability – just ask Jefferson. For those things, you need a drilled well.

The drilling of wells - as opposed to digging them - has been going on since the time of the ancient Chinese who, around 2,000 BC devised a bamboo framework from which a heavy chiseling tool was repeatedly raised and dropped, not so dissimilar from the modern cable drill still in use by some drillers today. As you might suspect, these ancient drills were somewhat on the slow side, but they have been credited with drilling wells up to 3,000 feet deep, albeit over generations.

Today, while cable drills are still in broad use, the preferred method is the rotary drill which, as its name suggests simply augers a hole into the earth like a giant power drill.

While cable drills can achieve tremendous depths, as demonstrated by the Chinese, most old wells that were drilled by cable drill tend not to be deep enough to satisfy modern demands. Many of these old wells were drilled before indoor plumbing, to say nothing of automatic washers, dishwashers, power washers, garden irrigation and the number of other things we have become accustomed to over the decades. In fact, the average American household uses 200-400 gallons of water per day.

[BELOW] A modern rotary well-drilling rig at work.

Figure 20   photo: Neil Shelton

Now, you may be thinking, "Gee whiz Neil, they tell me I ought to drink eight glasses of water a day, and I don't seem to be able to manage that, I really doubt if my family needs all that much water."

If you'll bear with me, I think you'll find that to be a rather short-sighted assumption.

When my wife and I first moved to this old farm back in the 70's there was an old 50- foot cable-drilled well which had supplied families since the 1920's. It seemed adequate for our needs, but (naturally) that summer was the driest our neighborhood had seen since blah, blah, blah, and no sooner did we get fully moved in, than the well went dry.

At that point we made a decision that we have not regretted once in the past forty years – we determined that we were going to have an everlasting supply of water, and we called a well-driller. Now, being perhaps a bit cynical, I was prepared for the drilling company to try to rip me off every way they could, so I was surprised — perhaps stunned might be a better word — when they started pulling up their equipment in half the time I was expecting. My well came in at 125 feet deep, 80 of which was solid rock, and it produces 33 gallons per minute. I won't bother talking about what the cost was because it was so long ago, but it wasn't very much — about a third of what could have been expected. As a result of nothing other than pure dumb luck, we had picked a spot on level ground near the base of a hill that proved simply ideal.

I'm not saying that I could tell you anything guaranteed to assure you of such luck, but it is a good idea to keep in mind what the water table in your area should look like, and to follow these rules:

Naturally, you want to locate the well close to the house so as to save on ditching and piping between the two, BUT before you drill you should make sure you know where any underground electrical cables may be and keep in mind that you'll need plenty of overhead room above the well site for the driller to set up his tall equipment and later if the pump needs to be pulled out of the well for maintenance.

Make certain that you locate your well away from potential pollutants such as septic tanks, leach fields, sewage lagoons or stockyards. If your property hasn't been surveyed yet, you should attend to that before you drill, and make certain that the well is at least ten feet inside your nearest boundary.

Be sure that your underground feed-lines to the house, and to any other faucets you plan, are buried below the frost line, and try to avoid running them under areas where sidewalks, patios or structures are planned. You may have to dig them up for maintenance sometime in the future.

Remember that in areas of adequate rainfall — that is, none-desert areas — the water table tends to follow the lay of the land, so if you are in hilly country, you'll do best to avoid drilling on the side of a hill, and you will probably, but not necessarily, get a better well at a shallower depth in a valley than on a hilltop.

Some people swear by "divining" or "dowsing", that is, the belief that one can locate a vein of water according to the actions of two sticks or rods held in the hands of the dowser, but then there used to be lots of people who felt it was better to be "thrown clear of the wreckage" than to wear seatbelts. Lest you have any doubts, both theories have been repeatedly disproved by science, so don't let anyone kid you about being able to find water with sticks.

If you knew exactly what the geologic formations were like under your property, locating the well would be a simple matter, but of course you don't. Your local well-drillers may have a reasonably-educated guess in many instances, but there's no surprise that exactly what's actually underground is a mystery to everyone.

That's not to say that you might not benefit from observing a few things about your property that might hint at where the best well location would be. For example, if we bear in mind that the top of the water table tends to mirror the contour of the land, then we might be able to expect a more plentiful supply of water near the base of a hill. Also for this reason, we'd want to drill on level ground, rather than into the side of a hill where we'd be drilling at an angle to the water table.

So while we can't really predict exactly where, or at what depth we'll get the most plentiful supply of water, we can be pretty certain that it will be on level land. We can also expect that a well located in a valley might produce a more reliable flow, possibly an artesian well, because the hill above the well is a virtual giant holding tank of water supply to take you through the dry spells.

[BELOW] Cross-section of a water table

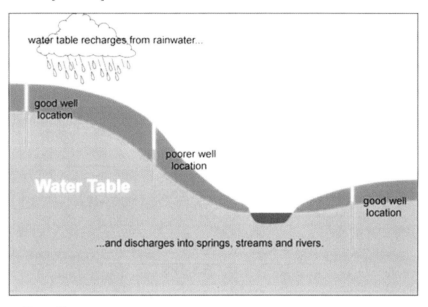

Figure 21   © Neil Shelton

Chapter 9: Pond Construction

Adding a farm pond to your property is probably the best thing you can do, short of building or drilling a well, to enhance the appraised value of your land, but the potential benefits to the landowner are far too valuable to express in terms of mere money. If you have the right soil and location, you can provide yourself and your great-grandkids with food, livestock water, recreation and beauty for lifetimes to come.

On the other hand, if your location isn't right, you'll be wasting machine-hire which can run $75 to $150 per hour while destroying part of the ecology of your place in the balance, so you'll want to check your site carefully before you proceed.

Soil Quality:

The most important aspect you need to consider is that of your soil's characteristics. In order for your pond to hold water, your soil needs to contain enough clay. To test this, dig a hole down through the brown or black top-soil into the sub-soil, which will be yellow, grey, or red in most locales. Once you've dug down that far, pick up samples and squeeze the soil in your hands. If it forms a firm ball that doesn't crumble easily, then this will make good material for your dam core. If the ball crumbles easily, then you'd probably be better off spending your pond-building money on something else.

Topography:

Obviously, you want a location where you can build the smallest dam that will do the job so an area where the topography forms as much of the sides of your pond as possible is best.

You also want the basin to be as wide and as flat as can be had. Try to keep your dam under twenty feet high, so as to keep costs down. Once you've flooded the area, you'll want there to be enough water depth to retard weed-growth.

When evaluating potential pond sites, look carefully at the drainage area above your proposed pond. If the slope is fairly gentle, then all you'll need is sod growing on your spillway, but if the watershed area is steep and large enough, it will require concrete covering the spillway to stop erosion during heavy rains.

Do NOT attempt to dam a flowing stream unless you are prepared to utilize prodigious amounts of concrete. Continuously flowing water, even a small amount, can cause massive erosion in only a short time, and small streams can become large torrents after a hard rain. At any rate, if fish production is important to you, avoid building on any spring or stream that will cause the water to continuously flow over the spillway as this will bring problems of silt accumulation and weed control. Also, spring-water flowing into the pond may lower the water temperature enough to hamper good fish production and growth.

[BELOW] A well-built pond can provide your property with beauty, recreation and food.

Figure 22

photo: Neil Shelton

Drainage Area:

The size of the drainage area is also critical. Most authorities suggest that the ratio of watershed area to pond surface area be about 10-15 to 1 if fish production is of prime importance. (If the pond is to be used for irrigation, or watering large numbers of animals, add more space accordingly to the drainage field.)

Avoid sites that drain barnyards, septic fields or roadways for obvious reasons.

You can boost your drainage area with the use of diversion ditches, but these should be used judiciously. It's more difficult to maintain a sod cover in many situations, especially at the ends of the ditch, and silt accumulation and erosion can quickly develop.

Pond Construction:

The machine of choice for pond-building is the bulldozer, although track loaders and even some wheel-loaders are used. Most custom machine operators will charge from $75 to

$150 per hour for a bulldozer, depending on the size of the machine. In my area the typical machine is the Caterpillar D6 and the typical price is $100 per hour.

While this can vary broadly depending on all the variables, one eight-hour day should get you a small pond, two days a good-sized one, and four or five days ought to yield something in the small-lake category (one-acre plus).

The first step is to have the dozer clear away everything, including trees, stumps, roots and sod from the pond site and the "borrow" area where you'll be taking out material to add to the dam core.

When that's done, you need to stake off the dam site, and remove the topsoil down to well within the subsoil. Push the top-soil aside for later use.

Also remove and stockpile the topsoil from the borrow area. Ideally, you'll leave one stockpile of topsoil below the dam and one above it.

Once the topsoil has been removed, excavate a trench directly under where the dam is to be. (See Figure 23) This trench, or "key", should span the entire length of the dam and up the adjoining hillsides to the height of the spillway.

If you want to use the pond for stock watering, it's strongly recommended that you run a pipe from inside the pond out to a watering trough downhill from the pond. If you want to add a water-tank supply, next dig a ditch perpendicular to the core trench or "cut-off" for the supply pipe. Remember that the ditch should be below the frost-line when it emerges from under the dam and the pipe used should be at least 1½ inches in diameter. This ditch provides a good place to put a drain pipe in your pond, a handy thing to have as you may want to completely drain the pond on infrequent occasions. Use a six or eight-inch pipe for this.

When the pipes are in place, it's time to start building up the dam. Use the best clay for the core, the next best for the front (water) side of the dam and what's left for the back side. Note again Figure 23: the front side of the dam should be at a 3:1 slope and the back side at a 2:1 slope; steeper than that, and you'll have problems with erosion.

The finished dam should be about three feet higher than the floor of the spillway, and at minimum eight feet wide at the top, but make it wider if you're able, as it is extremely handy to be able to drive a tractor or pick-up along the crest of the dam. Twelve-foot widths, or wider, are recommended.

[BELOW:] Cross-section of a properly-constructed pond bank.

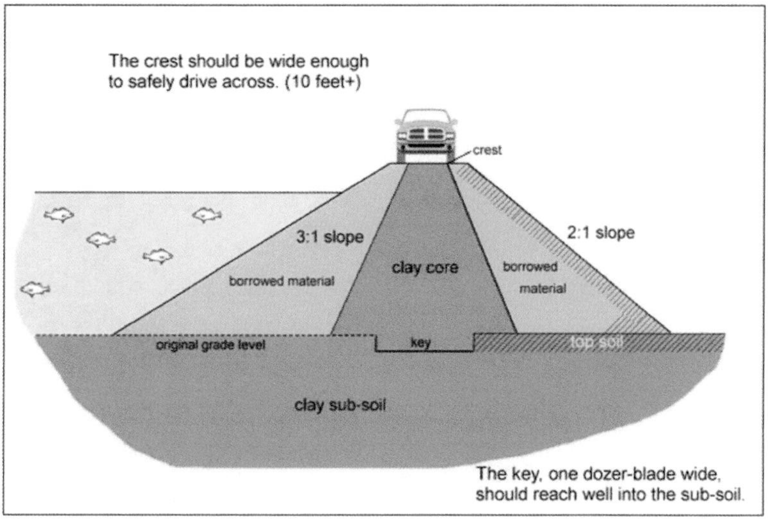

The crest should be wide enough
to safely drive across. (10 feet+)

crest

3:1 slope

2:1 slope

clay core

borrowed material

borrowed
material

original grade level

key

top soil

clay sub-soil

The key, one dozer-blade wide,
should reach well into the sub-soil.

Figure 23

© Neil Shelton

Spillway Construction:

If your dam is going to fail, it will most likely do so at the spillway, so mind how your spillway is constructed.

Above all, the spillway needs to be level at its mouth. Ideally, only a very shallow stream of water should move across the spillway so fish don't swim out during heavy rains. Make sure the spillway is wide enough to keep this stream at three inches or shallower, and so long and gently-sloping that the water moves as slowly as possible, again to discourage erosion.

Depending on the amount of watershed and the weather, even a good-sized pond may fill up with water in just one heavy storm, or it may take weeks or months. When it's half full or so, you can begin looking for fish to stock your new pond. In this area, fingerlings become available from the feed stores in the late spring to summer.

Chapter 10: How to Read Legal Descriptions

Everything You Always Wanted to Know About the Public Land Survey System, and Perhaps a Tiny Bit More

If you've ever wondered over the deed to your property, or the strange designations you've seen in your real-estate tax bill, you've come face to face with a legal description.

Ever since man started slicing up the earth and deciding which pieces of it belonged to whom, there has been a need for defining exactly where any given piece of land might lay. In early Britain, this was handled in a memorable fashion: the practice was to take a young child from the neighborhood, lead him one by one to the corners of the tract of land in question, then give him a severe thrashing at each location.

The theory was that the child would long remember each spot (if beaten with sufficient gusto) and could testify to its location long into the future.

Today's coddled children have it easy: we just record a survey at the County Recorder's Office, but when we walk around the perimeter of a property, we still call it, "beating the bounds". That's how the phrase originated.

In most of the United States, rural land is described according to what is referred to as the Public Land Survey System (PLSS), or less frequently, Government or Rectangle Survey, or *much* less frequently, the Aliquot system. It's used in thirty of the most rural states, including Alaska, but excluding Texas and the original thirteen colonies

Here's how that works: first all, a series of base-marks has been established for all of the continental U.S. Lines running north to south are referred to as "meridians" and east-west lines are called "base-lines".

Here's a map showing all the meridians and baselines:

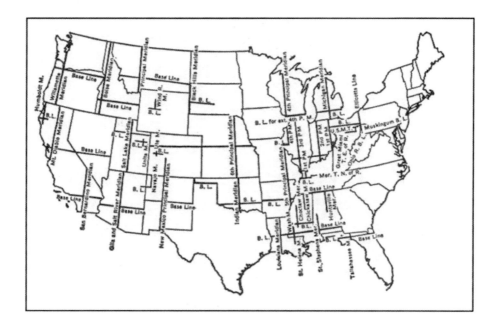

You'll notice that the Meridians converge as they go north. That, of course, is because of the curvature of the earth. Most of the effort involved in this sort of land description relates to different ways to describe squared boundaries on a spherical globe. It's like trying to put a postage stamp on an orange; you've got to figure out ways to iron out the wrinkles.

Starting from a baseline and a meridian line, Township Lines and Range Lines lay out a grid of 6-mile square blocks. For example, the first line 6 miles north of the Base Line is named Township 1 North of the Base Line, and the first line 6 miles west of the Meridian is Range 1 West of the Principle Meridian. The block that those two lines form is called Township 1 South, Range 1 East, or T1S,R1E.

Each Township and Range is further divided into 1-mile squares called Sections. The most important thing to remember about this stage of the process is that the 36 sections are numbered and arranged BOTH left to right AND right to left, as in Figure 27.

W1/2 NW1/4 NW1/4 Section 12 T28N, R8W 20 acres	NE1/4 NW1/4 NW1/4 Section 12 T28N, R8W 10 acres	NE1/4 NW1/4 Section 12 T28N, R8W 40 acres
	SE1/4 NW1/4 NW1/4 Section 12 T28N, R8W 10 acres	

NE 1/4 Section 12
T28N, R8W
160 acres

S1/2 NW1/4
Section 12
T28N, R8W
80 acres

12

| W1/2 SW1/4 Section 12 T28N, R8W 80 acres | E1/2 SW1/4 Section 12 T28N, R8W 80 acres | SE 1/4 Section 12 T28N, R8W 160 acres |

Then once you get inside a Section, that's when things really get interesting… or complicated, depending on your point of view. Each section can be divided into quarters and halves, so that a quarter-section is 160 acres and a quarter of a quarter is 40 acres. In Figure 28, the ten-acre square in the top of the northwest corner is described as "The Northeast Quarter of the Northwest Quarter of the Northwest Quarter of Section 12 Township 29N, Range 8 West" which is abbreviated NE1/4,NW1/4,NW1/4, S12 T29N R8W, or simply NW NW NW 12-29-8.

Got that? Okay, let's try it out. Suppose I want to look up a legal description that I've found on an old Warranty Deed: Here it is:

"All of the Southwest Quarter of the Southwest Quarter of the Southeast Quarter of Section 16, Township 29 North, Range 2 East."

The easiest way to decipher any legal description is to start at the end and work backward. Here's how we do that: In this case, we want to locate the property on a topo map, so we find the correct map by township and range, and we locate Section 16 in Township 29 North, Range 2 East. A typical section is one mile square and contains 640 acres.

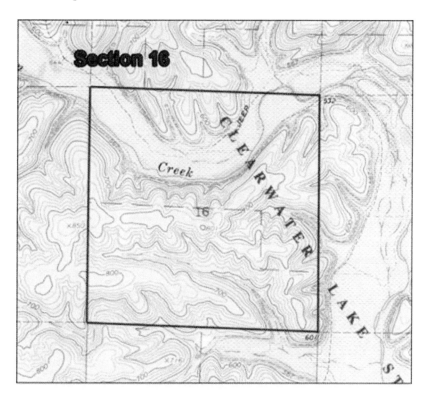

Next, we find the center of the section by drawing diagonals from each corner. Then we locate the Southeast Quarter of Section.16, as shown below. A typical Quarter Section is a half- mile square and contains 160 acres.

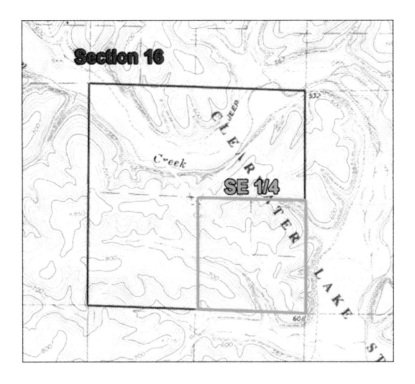

Using the same technique of drawing diagonals, we locate the Southwest Quarter of the Southeast Quarter of Section 16. A typical Quarter-Quarter Section is a quarter-mile square and contains 40 acres.

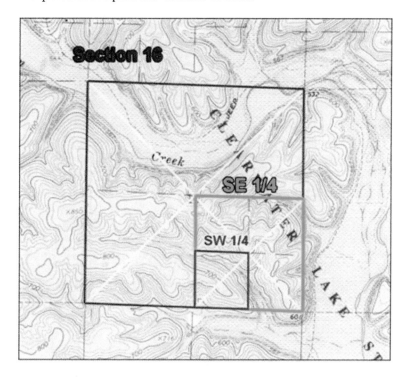

And finally, we locate the Northwest Quarter of the Southwest Quarter of the Southeast Quarter of Section 16, Township 29 North, Range 2 East. A typical Quarter-Quarter-Quarter Section is 660 feet square and contains 10 acres.

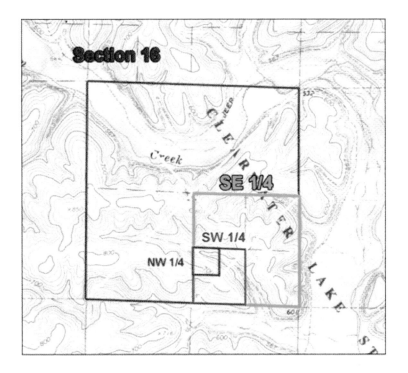

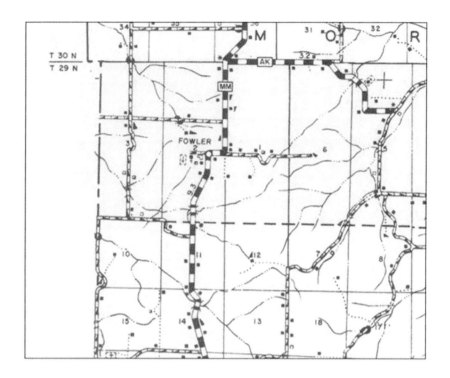

You'll notice that I keep using the term "typical section". Not all sections are the same size, especially those on the north and west side of a township block. These are frequently contracted or expanded to make up for the curvature of the earth. The yellow sections below are examples. These are in Texas County, Missouri. The sections along the northernmost tier of T 29 N are all about a mile wide by around 2-1/2 miles tall. Here's how this is handled:

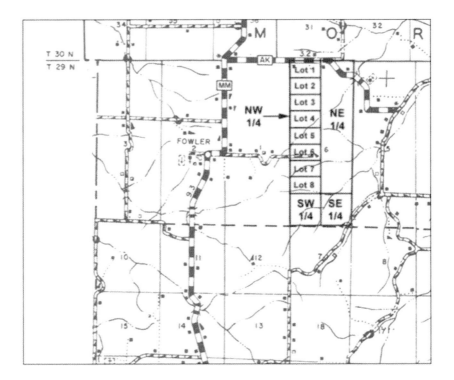

The southernmost Quarter Sections, the SW and the SE are of about normal size, around a half- mile square. However the remaining two miles is divided up into two so-called "quarters", the NW and the NE, and each of those is divided into eight "lots" of about 80 acres each. To complicate things, while this is the most common configuration for outsize sections, you may encounter others.

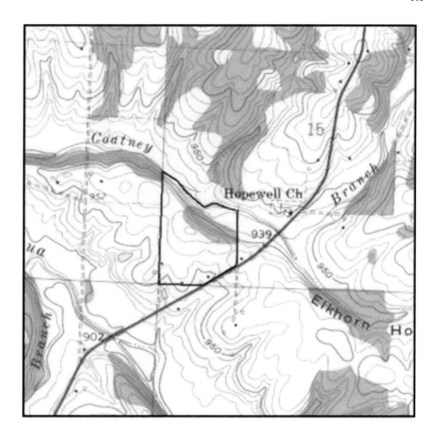

Quite often, a property description will describe an otherwise square tract which is bounded on one or more sides by a road or stream. In this case, a property such as the one shown below will be described as "All that part of the West Half of the Southwest Quarter of Section 15 lying south of Coatney Branch and north of Highway 73...

There are other systems of survey description most notably "Metes and bounds", which describes distances (metes) between different monuments (bounds). This method employs descriptions like, "Begin at the stone outcropping on the Elisha Wilson farm, thence proceed 15 rods north to a large hickory tree." The original thirteen American colonies as well as Kentucky, Tennessee, parts of Ohio, Maine and Vermont were divided using this method.

Now I'd like to end this discussion by saying something like, "and that's all there is to it." Unfortunately though, that's only the beginning. However, this will get you started, and you'll be able to talk to your county recorder without sounding too silly.

You'll also need to be familiar with a few terms of measurement that I've included below:

Linear Measure:

1 link = 7.92 inches

1 rod = 25 links = 16.5 feet

1 chain = 4 rods = 66 feet

1 furlong = 10 chains = 40 rods = 660 feet

1 mile = 8 furlongs = 80 chains = 320 rods = 5,280 feet

Area Measure:

1 square rod = 272¼ square feet (30¼ square yards) 1 square chain = 4,356 square feet

1 acre = 43,560 square feet

1 square mile = 640 acres (one section) 1 township x 1 range = 36 square miles

Chapter 11: How to Save a Bundle on Loan Interest

If you've ever borrowed money then you've had occasion to regret the amount of your lifestyle that was going to pay interest on your loan.

Nobody likes to pay interest, but chances are, unless you were born very, very rich or very, very poor, you are currently paying interest to someone on a loan for something..

We don't need to beat ourselves up over that. Because, without borrowed money, how many of us would have an education? How many would have a vehicle that starts every morning? How many would own a home?

Interest then, is the penalty that we pay for not being very, very wealthy, or very, very destitute.

Once we have accepted that trauma, we can move on to ask ourselves what can be done to minimize our exposure to interest, and as luck would have it, there are a several ways to make it easier to pay most any note off in reduced time at less expense and without adding too great a financial burden. I'm going to show you three.

That's not to say that the methods I'm about to demonstrate are any sort of free lunch, they aren't. You pay interest for the use of someone else's money, and these techniques work because you "rent" less of their money for a shorter period of time, i.e. you don't have as much borrowed or borrow it for so long.

Here are three ways to accelerate the payment of *almost* any amortized loan (almost, because some lenders don't allow you to make pre-payment) and each one is designed to reduce your interest charges, and have your note paid off as soon as possible in an affordable manner that has the least negative impact on your lifestyle.

All of the examples I've provided here are based on a typical 15-year loan of $10,000 bearing annual interest at the rate of 9% per year (per annum). (To manage your interest payments, you'll need an amortization schedule. If you don't want to make your own, you can find a few hundred thousand of them if you do an internet search on "free amortization schedule".)

Here's what an amortization schedule for our typical loan will look like:

Microsoft Excel - 9%amortization.xls							
File Edit View Insert Format Tools Data Window Help							
D183 *fx* =SUM(D2:D182)							
	A	B	C	D	E	F	G
1	date	beg. balance	payment	9% interest	principal	end bal.	
2	July 4, 2006	$10,000.00	$101.50	$75.00	$26.50	$9,973.50	
3	August 4, 2006	$9,973.50	$101.50	$74.80	$26.70	$9,946.80	
4	September 4, 2006	$9,946.80	$101.50	$74.60	$26.90	$9,919.90	
5	October 4, 2006	$9,919.90	$101.50	$74.40	$27.10	$9,892.80	
6	November 4, 2006	$9,892.80	$101.50	$74.20	$27.30	$9,865.50	
177	February 4, 2021	$469.54	$101.50	$3.52	$97.98	$371.56	
178	March 4, 2021	$371.56	$101.50	$2.79	$98.71	$272.85	
179	April 4, 2021	$272.85	$101.50	$2.05	$99.45	$173.40	
180	May 4, 2021	$173.40	$101.50	$1.30	$100.20	$73.20	
181	June 4, 2021	$73.20	$73.75	$0.55	$73.20	($0.00)	
182							
183			Total Interest Paid	$8,242.25			
184							
185							

In the top part of the window, you see the total amount borrowed, $10,000, and the computations for principle and interest are figured with each successive payment. Notice that the first month, when you make your first payment of $101.50, only $26.50 of your payment goes toward your equity -- that is, to decrease your debt -- and the rest, about 75%, goes to interest. Note that this situation gets progressively better with each succeeding payment so that fifteen years later, at the end of the loan (the bottom part of the window) almost all the payment goes toward equity with almost none of it going to interest.

It's important to note that the more extra principal (the part of your payment that goes to reduce your debt) you pay at the beginning of your loan, the more you save. Paying off principal will always lower interest charges, but the gains are multiplied over the life of the debt.

Obviously, things are going to be a lot more fun at the end of the loan than at the beginning, but paying a few extra dollars into your note early-on will reap impressive benefits later.

Just to demonstrate exactly how impressive, let's start out by making an extra $100 payment at the very beginning of the loan. That is, when you make out the check for your first payment, in this case instead of making the regular payment $101.50, you pay $201.50.

Here's what the amortization schedule looks like:

Microsoft Excel - 9%amortization-extra$100.xls

File　Edit　View　Insert　Format　Tools　Data　Window　Help

D180　　　▾　　　*fx* =SUM(D2:D178)

	A	B	C	D	E	F	G
1	date	beg. balance	payment	interest	principal	end bal.	
2	July 4, 2006	$10,000.00	$201.50	$75.00	$126.50	$9,873.50	
3	August 4, 2006	$9,873.50	$101.50	$74.05	$27.45	$9,846.05	
4	September 4, 2006	$9,846.05	$101.50	$73.85	$27.65	$9,818.40	
5	October 4, 2006	$9,818.40	$101.50	$73.64	$27.86	$9,790.53	
6	November 4, 2006	$9,790.53	$101.50	$73.43	$28.07	$9,762.46	
174	November 4, 2020	$400.28	$101.50	$3.00	$98.50	$301.78	
175	December 4, 2020	$301.78	$101.50	$2.26	$99.24	$202.55	
176	January 4, 2021	$202.55	$101.50	$1.52	$99.98	$102.57	
177	February 4, 2021	$102.57	$101.50	$0.77	$100.73	$1.83	
178	March 4, 2021	$1.83	$1.85	$0.01	$1.84	($0.00)	
179							
180			Total Interest Paid	$7,965.85			
181							
182							

Now let's see how much good that extra $100 did for us. Plenty.
Fifteen years later, at the end of the loan you've saved $280.95 in interest paid, and you've retired your debt three months early! All this for a hundred bucks.
So you can see that, if you can pay a bit more than the program calls for,

you can save yourself a nice bit of change.

Now that you've got the hang of how it works, let's investigate the three strategies to save on interest.

#1 Switch to Bi-weekly Payments *Saves 815 days and $1,412*

How it's done: Instead of making the regular monthly payments according to the amortization schedule, you make half a payment every two weeks.

What it costs: Making half a payment twice per month doesn't in itself cost anything and will *save you $188* or so over the fifteen-year term. What we're doing, however is paying every 14 days so that, because there are enough weeks in the year to make up thirteen months, you actually pay one extra month's payment per year more than you're scheduled to.

```
Microsoft Excel - 9%amortizationevery-14days.xls
File  Edit  View  Insert  Format  Tools  Data  Window  Help
D336          fx =SUM(D2:D333)
```

	A	B	C	D	E	F	G
1	date	beg. balance	payment	interest	principal	end bal	
2	July 4, 2006	$10,000.00	$50.75	$34.62	$16.13	$9,983.87	
3	July 18, 2006	$9,983.87	$50.75	$34.56	$16.19	$9,967.67	
4	August 1, 2006	$9,967.67	$50.75	$34.50	$16.25	$9,951.43	
5	August 15, 2006	$9,951.43	$50.75	$34.45	$16.30	$9,935.13	
6	August 29, 2006	$9,935.13	$50.75	$34.39	$16.36	$9,918.77	
328	January 1, 2019	$282.14	$50.75	$0.98	$49.77	$232.37	
329	January 15, 2019	$232.37	$50.75	$0.80	$49.95	$182.42	
330	January 29, 2019	$182.42	$50.75	$0.63	$50.12	$132.30	
331	February 12, 2019	$132.30	$50.75	$0.46	$50.29	$82.01	
332	February 26, 2019	$82.01	$50.75	$0.28	$50.47	$31.54	
333	**March 12, 2019**	$31.54	$31.65	$0.11	$31.54	$0.00	
335							
336		Total Interest Paid	$6,829.90				
337							
338							

The Results: Paying every fourteen days, you pay your loan off 2¼ years early and you save $1,412.35 in interest fees.

Hint: You might also want to consider that you'll be making 180 more payments which *might* incur other costs, like postage or credit card fees. These days, many lenders offer on-line payment options.

#2 Make a Payment Every Three Weeks. *Saves 2,551 days and $4,199*

How it's done: Instead of making the regular monthly payments according to the amortization schedule, you pay the monthly amount every 21 days. It feels like a monthly payment, but you're speeding your payback considerably.

What it costs: You make 5-1/3 more payments ($541) in a year's time than you would paying the regular monthly amortization.

The Results: Paying every three weeks, you pay your loan off seven years *early,* and you save $4,198.96.

	Microsoft Excel - 9%amortizationevery-21days.xls

File Edit View Insert Format Tools Data Window Help

D142   ▾   *fx* =SUM(D2:D141)

	A	B	C	D	E	F	G
1	date	beg. balance	payment	interest	principal	end bal.	
2	July 4, 2006	**$10,000.00**	**$101.50**	$51.92	$49.58	$9,950.42	
3	July 25, 2006	$9,950.42	$101.50	$51.67	$49.83	$9,900.59	
4	August 15, 2006	$9,900.59	$101.50	$51.41	$50.09	$9,850.50	
5	September 5, 2006	$9,850.50	$101.50	$51.15	$50.35	$9,800.14	
6	September 26, 2006	$9,800.14	$101.50	$50.89	$50.61	$9,749.53	
136	March 18, 2014	$436.15	$101.50	$2.26	$99.24	$336.91	
137	April 8, 2014	$336.91	$101.50	$1.75	$99.75	$237.16	
138	April 29, 2014	$237.16	$101.50	$1.23	$100.27	$136.89	
139	May 20, 2014	$136.89	$101.50	$0.71	$100.79	$36.11	
140	June 10, 2014	$36.11	$36.30	$0.19	$36.11	($0.01)	
141							
142			Total Interest Paid	$4,043.29			
143							
144							

#3 Double Up on Your Principal Payments *Saves 2,709 days and $4,087*

How it's done: Print out an amortization schedule for your loan. Each time you make a payment for the current month, include next month's principal amount in the check as well.

Then cross both months off the list. Each time you do this, you save yourself a month over the amortization schedule.

What it costs: At first, your payments are only a bit higher than the regular amortization, in the case given, the first month's payment goes from $101.50 to $127.95 whereas   your last few payments before your early pay-off are nearly twice what the original monthly payment was.

The Results: Paying double principal payments, you pay your loan in half the time (7½ years) and you save $4,087.17.

	Microsoft Excel - 9%amortizationdoubleprincipal.xls						
	File Edit View Insert Format Tools Data Window Help						
	D94 ▼ *fx* =SUM(D2:D93)						
	A	B	C	D	E	F	G
1	date	beg. balance	payment	interest	principal	end bal.	
2	July 4, 2006	$10,000.00	$127.95	$75.00	$52.95	$9,947.05	
3	August 4, 2006	$9,947.05	$128.35	$74.60	$53.75	$9,893.30	
4	September 4, 2006	$9,893.30	$128.75	$74.20	$54.55	$9,838.75	
5	October 4, 2006	$9,838.75	$129.16	$73.79	$55.37	$9,783.38	
6	November 4, 2006	$9,783.38	$129.58	$73.38	$56.20	$9,727.18	
88	September 4, 2013	$815.55	$197.13	$6.12	$191.01	$624.54	
89	October 4, 2013	$624.54	$198.57	$4.68	$193.88	$430.66	
90	November 4, 2013	$430.66	$200.03	$3.23	$196.80	$233.86	
91	December 4, 2013	$233.86	$201.51	$1.75	$199.76	$34.10	
92	January 4, 2014	$34.10	$34.36	$0.26	$34.10	($0.00)	
93							
94			Total Interest Paid	$4,155.08			
95							
96							

It's important to remember when making advance payments, that even if you're paid a year ahead, you're still obligated to make the monthly payments unless you've made other arrangements with your lender.

Chapter 12: Foreclosure: Both Sides

There's a certain security about owning land: you can figure that, once you've acquired title to real property, then as long as you keep the real estate taxes paid, no-one can take it away from you. That is, they can't take it without your permission, and that permission is exactly what most loan or mortgage documents give the lender — legal permission to take your land if you don't pay back the money you've been loaned..

That's virtually unavoidable when you borrow large sums, such as you might need to buy the land in the first place, because banks are definitely for-profit institutions, and no bank will loan money unless they have some protection in the event that the borrower doesn't pay. Of course, no-one takes out a loan planning to default, but because things don't always work out the way we plan them, most anyone can find themselves facing foreclosure if the winds of circumstance blow in the wrong direction.

That's why you need to know a little about how foreclosure works, and what you can do if you find yourself in this position.

First, a little bit about how the mechanics of foreclosure:

Whether you own unimproved land, or a fully-equipped farm, your debt is probably evidenced, that is, formalized in writing, by one of three legal instruments. Which one your lender has used will have quite a bit to do with your rights, and how quickly the lender can enact foreclosure.

Lease with Option to Buy: If you're buying the land on a lease-with-option, then you probably don't have much in the way of protection against the lender or seller retaking possession of the property should you stop paying. You have the rights of a tenant, and if you get behind on the payments, those rights can disappear like a wisp of smoke, depending on the wording of the lease agreement, which is typically and understandably most favorable to the seller.

Generally speaking, if you fall a month or two behind, there's no reason to assume you have any ownership rights at all. The seller may give you formal notice of your delinquency, but not necessarily — perhaps not even if you catch up later. Of particular concern about leases-with-option is this: if, when you bought the property, the seller may not have had clear title - or even any title at all — this would not necessarily have kept him from making a deal with you as long as he felt confident that he could provide you with clear title when you'd paid enough to exercise your option. In other words, if you have a lease with option to buy, and you're having difficulty in making regular payments, there may very well be a third party you are unaware of exerting pressure on the landlord, who may decide, and correctly so, that the best way to keep *himself* out of trouble is to declare *you* in default, thus ending any claim you have against the property.

Contract for Deed: Better for you than a lease, but not by much, especially if it hasn't been recorded. This contract probably hasn't been recorded at the county, which means that foreclosure can be accomplished rather more quickly, perhaps with just a letter to you stating that by failing to pay in timely fashion, you have lost all rights to the property. Contracts for Deed are also used frequently by sellers who can't immediately give clear title, so there's a high likelihood that a third party actually holds a mortgage on the property and, again, the person you bought it from can keep himself out of trouble most easily by declaring a default putting you out of the picture.

Mortgage or Deed of Trust: This will be the documentation used for most transactions, including virtually all of those managed by regular banks or loan companies. In the typical case, you will have a certain set of fairly standardized rights, and the foreclosure procedure will follow a general guideline prescribed by state law. This is the type of documentation and foreclosure that we'll be addressing here for the most part. If you're interested in the most gruesome of the details, look up foreclosure laws for your particular state, but generally speaking, after a period of non-payment, the lender will send you a letter or perhaps a series of letters, advising you that you need to get caught up - pronto. If they don't hear or receive anything from you at that point, after around sixty to ninety days, you can expect some legal notice that the property is going into foreclosure, which typically will be a process which may or may not involve state courts, and may include having a Sherriff's sale which will be advertized in a local newspaper, perhaps mentioning your name.

If you find yourself facing foreclosure...

At this point we should mention that, if you find yourself unable to keep up your payments on any of these three types of loans, the first thing you should do is the same in every case, and that is to devise the best plan you can to get yourself to a point where you can again start making payments, and when you have devised this plan, go to your lender and try to sell him on your idea. A good basis for such a plan might be to offer to keep up just the interest on the note until you can get back on your feet, but the most important aspect of your plan must be that it represents *something you can reasonably hope to fulfill.* If you offer a reduced- payment plan, then can't keep up with that, you can't expect much more leniency.

The importance of speaking to, and staying in close touch with, the lender cannot be overemphasized. Your situation means that you have failed to perform on a contract, and the lender is empowered to seize the property on fairly short notice. He is much less likely to do this if you are speaking with him, preferably face-to-face, offering a reasonable solution to the problem. In other words, he has to look you in the eye on a regular basis.   You may persuade him to let you catch up in a set amount of time, or even to modify the terms of the loan, depending on the situation. If you have a home on the property, and you have some hope of coming current sometime in the not-too-distant future, you may find a government program that will assist you, or if all else fails, you may choose to avail yourself of either Chapter 7 or Chapter 13 bankruptcy, which will give you time get your affairs in order while keeping your home, but not all the acreage.

If your situation is hopeless, that is, you don't have the money now, and you see no viable way that you will be able to raise it in the foreseeable future, then your only real option is to accept that fact, and offer the lender a deed to the property in lieu of foreclosure, which will make things easier on him and keep the matter out of the courts.

You might be asking yourself why, when you're the one taking the big loss, you should worry yourself about making things easy for the lender. The answer is that in doing so, you're also helping yourself.

Remember, old movies where the villain wants to throw Little Nell out into the snow? Well, melodrama notwithstanding, your lender in all likelihood really doesn't *want* to foreclose you. What he wants is to get his money, and failing that, to keep his costs at a minimum. Foreclosure of a mortgage or Deed of Trust will cost him anywhere from a thousand dollars to several times that much, and will take up several months, or even a couple of years, during which time the property is at risk and in limbo.

If you give him a Quit-claim Deed giving up your claim to the property, then he'll probably spend less than $100 getting the property back, and he'll have your assurance that you'll leave in timely fashion without doing damage, as some less-honest people might.

In return for this, you may save yourself from having a judgment filed against you should the foreclosure not result in a bid equal or greater than what you owed, and perhaps you can even avoid a negative mark on your credit report.

(A word of caution is in order: if you ever had any doubt that it is a cold, cruel world out there, perhaps it will be erased when you learn that the Internal Revenue Service considers your heart-wrenching situation as a fortunate (and taxable) gain on your behalf. Because, if you had the money to pay your mortgage, and you then make a deal to cancel that loan, all the money you would have spent paying your debt, had you had any, can now theoretically be spent on bon-bons and jewelry (lucky you). So, depending on where you live, and your other tax obligations, they may very well consider that if the bank cancels your $50,000 debt, then you must be $50,000 richer, and you should therefore be taxed on an extra fifty grand of income for the year.)

Another solution would be to find another buyer for the property who can either pay-off the debt, or if your lender is agreeable, assume it. While this does happen on occasion, it requires making a very fast sale, which is something that generally *doesn't* occur all that frequently in the real estate business, especially during hard times. You can try listing the property with an agent, but unless you can offer a very attractive price, that isn't likely to result in a sale in the short time you have. If you know a friend, acquaintance, or relative who's ever expressed interest in owning your property, now is the time to talk to them.

Those are the facts of foreclosure, and frankly, they're pretty grim. At risk of being repetitive, your best luck will lie in getting in touch with your lender early and often, and in showing him that you're doing everything you possibly can. Do NOT waste time and money on private companies that claim that they can help you stop foreclosure. They can't.

If you have to foreclose a real estate debt...

If you own land, then you're likely to one day want to sell land... and if you sell land, it's also likely that you may choose to finance all or part of the sale... and if that happens, then there's the very real possibility that you may find yourself in the position of having to foreclose the debt to take back legal title or possession to the property for lack of payment.

This isn't a very pleasant process, but of course it's better than being foreclosed-on oneself. The best outcome you can hope for is to get your property back with a minimum of damage and with the fewest ill-feelings possible.

When giving this advice in person, I have, on a few regrettable occasions encountered a question that goes something like this: "What do I care about 'ill feelings'"? These no-goods made a deal, and now they won't (or can't) deliver."

If this sounds like you, then I hope you won't ever finance a piece of property again.

Nobody goes into a land purchase planning to lose everything they've invested, and you, as the lien-holder, shouldn't take their failure as a personal affront to yourself. If you can't see any wisdom in not being a jerk, there's probably nothing I could say to discourage you, but I hope you'll treat everyone the way you'd want (not expect) to be treated were the roles reversed.

It is not at all common, when you're financing a piece of property, for the buyer to encounter a period of time when he has problems making the payments. If he's smart, he'll contact you as soon as he knows that this situation exists, or is imminent, and offer you a deal for adjusting his payments temporarily. I advise you to take his offer if it doesn't last for more than a few months, and if he continues to make a regular payment of a reduced amount during the duration.

It may be that you don't hear from him at all, no payments, no comments, no nothing. If this is the case, I suggest contacting him when the payment becomes a couple of weeks past due. While it's rare, people actually DO forget to make their payments, or he may have a situation where he'll be able to pay shortly, and was hoping you wouldn't notice. In any case, you should be sympathetic, but firm. After all, you may very well need the income to keep yourself from a similar situation.

If it becomes obvious that your buyer just isn't capable of continuing to make payments, then it's time for you to step in and end it. How you do this depends, as usual, on the documentation you have on the loan, but first, in every case, you need to send the buyer some form of communication stating your intentions and advising him as to what he can do to keep the property. In all likelihood, all that would be acceptable at this point is for him to pay you off completely in cash. If so, say so, and give the amount required for pay-off. It is important that you keep a copy of this letter, and proof of when it was sent. Ask the Post Office to send it " certified, return receipt" so you will have proof that he received this notice.

Your contract, Deed of Trust, or mortgage will specify exactly when the loan officially goes into default, and it goes without saying that you should give at least that amount of time before beginning the foreclosure process.

If the loan was made by a contract for deed, or lease with option, either of which was not recorded, all you really need to do is announce to the buyer that you are retaking possession of the property. You should keep in mind that the buyer may have recorded the contract himself — this isn't very common, but it does happen. In that case, you'll need some method of clearing the title; if you can't get him to sign a Quit-claim Deed to you, you may need to hire an attorney and make a mental note that the next time you sell a property on credit, you're going to use the methods I outline in this chapter.

If you're holding a mortgage or Deed of Trust, then the conventional way to handle this is to hire an attorney to foreclose the note for you. This, of course is expensive and time-consuming, as with most things that require legal counsel.

There is one way, however, that you can avoid the actual foreclosure process. That is if you can convince the buyer to give you a Quit-claim Deed to the property in return for your releasing him from his debt.

There are at least two reasons why he might want to do this. First, he might choose to sign a Quit-claim Deed because you have been so kind and polite in dealing with him, and he realizes that you're a regular human being just like him, and you're only trying to make the best of a bad situation.

Second, he may understand that the fact that you take back the property through foreclosure does not mean that he doesn't still owe you the money. That's right, as mentioned earlier, you can, conceivably take back the property through foreclosure, then sue him to collect on the debt. It may be unlikely that you would be successful in this suit, but the possibility exists.

If you are able to obtain a Quit-claim Deed, you're not quite done there. You also need to file a Full Deed of Release with the county to clear the title. Record this after you record the Quit-claim Deed. Some title companies will insist on this release before they will insure title and some won't, but since title standards tend to get more stringent as time goes on, rather than less, it's a good idea to clear the matter up early when it will only cost you the price of recording.

Bidding at a Sheriff's Sale

Purchasing land at a Sheriff's sale, or Trustee's sale maybe a way to buy land for a bargain price, or it can be something else if you're not careful.

However, this is a venue where hardball is played. In a typical real estate purchase, the buyer enjoys certain guarantees and assumptions that do not necessarily apply to public auctions. I recently encountered a case where a young couple with an inheritance wished to make the most of their money, which they decided could be done by buying land in foreclosure through a Sheriff's sale. Once they found a likely candidate, a few acres with a rather nice cabin on it, they pooled all their funds and gave the auction their best shot. There wasn't a great deal of competition, and theirs was the winning bid.

Had they chosen to purchase property through an agent, or directly from the owner, they almost certainly would have received information about where the property boundaries were, or if they didn't, they might have had recourse against the agent or the seller. However, as bidders at the Sheriff's sale, they were responsible for making their own investigation of the property at their own risk.

When the couple went to visit the property, they pulled into the driveway, got out of their car and assumed that everything they saw: a cabin, a well, a barn and a small spring, were all on the property.

Unfortunately, the previous owner, the one who lost the property to the bank, had originally purchased two parcels of land adjoining one another. When it came time to build the cabin, both parcels had been paid off, so a building loan was taken out, but only the parcel where the cabin was to be built was mortgaged. The spring, well, and barn were all on the unencumbered parcel, which was not part of the collateral on the loan.

So then, when the bank repossessed the cabin, neither any bank personnel nor our fledgling land buyers, saw a need to survey the property, which survey would have made it clear that only the cabin was located on the foreclosed property, and that by only a few inches. In other words, the former owner still had title to the second parcel along with the spring, well, and barn. A new well would need to be drilled before the young couple could even move in.

Paying for a survey of property that one was only planning to bid on with no guarantee that one would win the bid would be a gamble in itself, but anyone with the ability to read the land's legal description, then find the property on Google Earth, could easily have seen that the property in our example was spread out over a larger area than that being offered for sale.

Chapter 13: How to Sell Your Land Yourself and Move on With Your Life.

There is no other single aspect of land ownership which more completely captures the imagination than the actual selection and purchase of the land.

Sometimes however, on the way to acquiring the ideal tract of land, many folks, for whatever reasons, wind up owning the less-than-ideal parcel that needs to be sold before real- property nirvana can be achieved.

Whether you inherited a piece of property that doesn't mesh with your goals, discovered that you simply need to live in another part of the world, or even if you bought a piece of property and later just fell out of love with it, selling land, particularly in a poor market, can appear to be a daunting task. The amateur's first reaction is usually to list with a real estate agent and hope for the best.

Now, far be it from me to discourage using an agent. This certainly is the easiest way and not necessarily the least profitable or most expensive, especially in a booming market. In a less-than-booming market however, it's good to remember that listing your property with an agent will subject it to comparison with dozens, perhaps hundreds of other listings, all competing with yours in features and price. Selling your property then, will probably require that a potential buyer finds it to be either the best he sees… or the cheapest.

If you have unimproved land to sell, you may also find that the majority of agents are more interested in selling more expensive improved properties where they stand to make much larger commissions (and get fewer ticks) so your five acres of woods may get short shrift when it comes to exposure to the market. This wouldn't be such a big problem were it not for the fact that these days, more and more brokers are insisting on exclusive listing contracts that obligate you to pay them a commission even if you sell the property yourself to the fellow next door.

That's why you may want to tackle the job on your own. These days, you can set your land apart from the crowd by marketing and selling it yourself. Since the advent of the internet, it's easier and more effective than ever, and the phrase "for sale by owner" has a particular cachet about it that buyers seem to like. Many buyers assume that they'll be saving the sales commission by buying directly from the owner. Of course, you're probably assuming that *you're* saving the sales commission by selling it yourself. Which of you is correct depends on how adeptly you handle your sale.

Evaluating Your Land from a Seller's Standpoint

The first step is to decide on your price. The timid choose a price too low, and the foolish pick one too high. What you want to do is find the right price that will yield a reasonably quick sale, but not generate a stampede of skinflints to your door.

To determine, or appraise, the value of land, you need comparables. Using the internet, finding these is easier than it's ever been, although there are also a few new pitfalls.

The best places to find your comparables are the places where you plan to advertise. In a moment I'm going to recommend that you advertise on the internet, so you shouldn't be surprised if that's where I recommend you gather your comparables as well.

In choosing comparables, you want as many tidbits of information as you can find; that's the primary reason why the web is the best source, because the people writing the advertisements there aren't usually paying by the word - although you'll find that they can still be infuriatingly vague.

Here are the basic things that must be considered when appraising land:

Size: The fact that you find 80 acres, or 8,000 acres, selling for a given amount per acre tells you virtually nothing about what your 8 acres is worth, so ignore it. Rather, classify your property somewhat like this: is it from 0 to 3 acres? 3 to 8? 8 to 15? 15 to 40? Of course it can't be all that cut-and-dried, but remember to only compare your rural property to others of about the same size – nothing has greater bearing on the value of unimproved land than size, except, to a degree, location.

Please note that I am NOT going to repeat the old saw about the three most important things to know about real estate. Unless you spent your formative years in a cave, you've already heard it enough times to make you wish you hadn't.

I'll assume that, as an adult who can read and operate a computer, you already know that the price of your 40 acres in western Kansas has very little to do with the value of New York's Central Park, but you do need to make a distinction between a property that's a thirty-minute drive from a city and one that's two hours distant.

I've found that most people draw an invisible line at a thirty-minute commute whether they're commuting into L.A. or Buzzard's Bluff.

Additionally, you shouldn't compare land from outside your region. West-coast prices aren't applicable to West Virginia, and vice versa.

Okay, that takes care of the broadest measures. Let's assume you're looking for comparable land to your forty acres in rural Tennessee, we next start to evaluate the features of the land.

Water: Lake or river frontage is more valuable to most people than a non-navigable stream, which is more valuable than a spring, which is more valuable than a pond, which is more valuable than no water at all. Almost everyone wants water frontage, but not everyone is willing to pay for it.

Soil, Terrain, and Vegetation: Most small landowners will prefer a mixture of hill and valley, but level agricultural land is usually more expensive than hilly ground. However, if your property is smaller, say less than eighty acres, there will probably be a better market for the mixed terrain that includes level bottomland and forested hills. Likewise, the best overall market exists for small properties with a mixture of forest and meadow as opposed to all woods or all field.

Improvements: A modern water-well is worth more than it costs to drill. In the Ozarks, for example, where the typical well costs around $6,000, I generally value them at around $10K.

Access: While few in number, there are still some properties that don't have legal access – that is, a deeded access-easement, or frontage on a public road. This is what is known as "landlocked" property, and it is of considerably less value. If you see an extremely low-priced piece of land for sale, it may be a bargain, or it may just not have legal access. Curing this can be fairly simple, but don't count on it. If it were an easy matter, it would likely already have been fixed. In most cases, legal access will require a deed from the neighbor whose land you're crossing, and folks tend not to like to sign deeds unless they get something of significant value in return.

Utilities: Electric and phone. Check whether your comparables have, or don't have, the same utilities that your property has. If not, and all other things are equal, price yours ahead of those that don't have what yours does, or behind those that have what yours doesn't.

Buildings: This chapter is intended to address land-only sales. Obviously, if your land has buildings on it, those can add significantly to the value. If the buildings are of any value, that is, a livable house or a barn or shed in good repair, this may be harder for you to estimate or to compare with others. About the best you can hope to do is to compare the number of rooms/bedrooms, the square footage, the general condition, and overall appearance.

If the buildings are of marginal value, give them appropriate ranking, however as advice to a potential seller of real estate (I'd tell a potential buyer something else) don't discount that shack or hovel too severely. A lot of buyers seem to feel somehow assured if there's a structure of any kind on a property. Maybe it seems less intimidating than starting with empty woods. So if it doesn't leak too badly, and isn't going to fall down in the next few years, you may consider bumping the price up a few thousand dollars, or leaving it where it is so that the building provides another inducement to buy.

Finally after you've researched all your research and compared all your comparables, it's time to decide on your final price.

Actually, this is the easy part: you bring all your comparables together and rank them – a spreadsheet like Excel is good for this. Put the price of each property in Column A, the "sort" column, and a brief description of the features in Column B.

Now put yourself in a buyer's shoes. Right away, you can see what's a bargain and what may be overpriced. The idea is to price your property as a happy median between the two extremes.

Advertising/Marketing

Now that you've arrived at your price, you're ready to put your property in front of the world. To do this, the first thing you need is a web page.

Now, I suppose you could HIRE someone to make a page for you, but frankly, if you can read well enough to get this far in this book, you're perfectly capable of making one on your own.

Nowadays all of my favorite software packages come for the same price: free. So I'd check out what's available at tucows.com or software.com.

You can also make a tolerable web page using Microsoft Word (which probably came loaded on your computer) however, if you've never made any web pages before, you'll probably also be needing web-space to put them on, and you can find both web-authoring software and web-space available cheap or free with a little thoughtful web-searching.

Once you've got the mechanics taken care of, all you need to do is collect absolutely everything you can think of that will describe your property, which may include, but will not be limited to, a written description, lots and lots of photographs, perhaps taken in different seasons, information about the local area, last year's real estate taxes, aerial photos, road maps and perhaps a .pdf or .jpg copy of the survey, if available.

Next, it's time to advertise. Depending somewhat on the type and location of your property, you can find a handful of free advertising sites on the web and you should employ these, preferably with a link to your web-page(s) if that's permitted. However, few of these free sites bring you enough traffic to help much in the absence of some uncommonly good luck.

That means, as it always has, that you're going to have to pay for your advertising just as sellers always have, but take heart in the fact that you don't have to pay nearly as much for national advertising as you did in the days of paper. Better still, if you put a hit-counter on your web page(s), you'll be able to keep track of how much traffic you get from each source. That will give you an idea of which ads are most effective.

Personally, I've had good experience with Google Adwords where you can set your ad budget to as little as one dollar per day. (You may be able to set it even lower, but let's get serious, you DO want to sell this place don't you? Adwords also coordinates with Google Analytics ®, which will tell you far more than you need to know about the traffic you're getting to your pages. Also provided are ways to see how effective the ads you write are proving to be.

LandWatch.com is another favorite source of mine which consistently supplies better-quality leads, that is, more serious clients, than Google and others.

Financing

Now it's time for probably the toughest decision you'll have to make about selling your property. Do you want to finance the price, or will you only accept cash in full?

Perhaps I can help you out with that decision. If you finance, you are going to have a LOT more prospective customers than if you don't, and if you make the terms easy enough, you will have even more.

That's not to say that there aren't a few potential hazards involved in owner-financing, but in my view, the benefits far out-weigh the drawbacks.

t first you may think that owner-financing means giving up all the money you expected to realize when your property sells, but if you look at it from the long-term view, you'll actually make about twice as much at competitive interest rates.

One of the first benefits of this is that when you collect interest on your sale proceeds, unlike an interest-bearing bank account, the interest on your land sale starts out as a large percentage of the payment and shrinks over the life of the loan. So the first payments made to you largely go toward interest.

Moreover, even though you'll not have a lump sum of money to place against another piece of land or some other big-ticket item such as a vehicle or home construction, you will have the guaranteed income to match your payments, or some such new purchases, including the interest. You'll also get to keep a lot more of the money you'll receive, because you'll only pay income taxes in small installments over the years, rather than all at once, which is likely to bump you into a higher tax bracket.

"But," you're probably thinking, "this 'guaranteed income' is only guaranteed by another individual — a human being just like myself and subject to all the same problems, foibles and weaknesses. What if my buyer defaults?."

That is a very realistic concern. Here's a system I've devised that works well for me:

To begin with, when I place my advertisements I make two assumptions: first, I assume that my buyer will want me to finance the sale, because this is the case about 95% of the time.

Second, I assume that my buyer may very well default, especially in the first six months, because this happens about 25-30% of the time.

These two assumptions prepare me mentally for the task ahead, and they prepare me physically to guide in the preparation of the documents I will use to consummate the deal.

I accept a no-down-payment deal — only the first monthly installment is required to cement the deal. (I offer a discount for cash.)

The deal I make is that the transaction is governed for the critical first six months by a Contract for Deed. That is, the title stays with me, if the buyer defaults, he simply loses his money, the deal is off, and everyone goes back to square one.

However, after the buyer makes his sixth payment, I give him title to the property, that is I make and record a Warranty Deed to him, and hold a Promissory Note and Deed of Trust in return as security. Finally, as boiler-plate, I have the buyer sign a Quit-claim Deed back to me which is annotated to only be recorded in the event of a default. This, in one stroke lowers my foreclosure costs from around $1,500 to hire an attorney to perform a trustee's sale, down to about $27 to record the Quit-claim Deed. Since I create all the contracts and deeds myself from standard forms, I save immensely on attorney's fees. Using this technique, I am prepared both for the long-term sale as well as, should it be necessary, a fast and easy foreclosure.

Preparing the Property

Finally, you need to get the property into shape to show it to prospects. There's probably not a lot you can do in this regard. This being unimproved land, it tends to rise and fall on its own inherent virtues or faults. The good news is that there's probably not a lot that needs to be done. I'd recommend though that you consider three areas:

The Road: The better the condition of the access road, the better impression your property will make. If your land is three miles of bad county-road away from pavement, then I wouldn't waste a lot of money making the access from the county road any better than the county road itself, but remember that you can do quite a bit to civilize a dirt driveway with a tractor and blade. If you don't have too much length to cover, there's no substitute for a layer of 1" crushed rock (or larger rock in deep mud-holes). One layer of 1" rock one lane wide will cost you about 75¢ per foot around my neighborhood. Needless to say, if the property is on a road maintained by the county, or some other local government entity, and if this road has any work that needs to be done, this is an excellent time to complain politely about it to the wonderful folks on the Road Board. Most counties grade their roads once or twice a year, but some roads that don't get much traffic may be neglected if no-one complains.

Clean Up the Junk: If you didn't do this when you bought the place, now is the time. Other than buildings of value, get rid of everything that didn't grow there. This doesn't have to be a major ordeal. First check out local laws regarding what, if anything, can be burned at your location. Nearly all states have laws against burning old tires and many forbid burning other items such as other rubber products; wire; treated, painted or finished wood; plastics; garbage; heavy oils; asphalt materials; building materials, especially those containing asbestos; paints; and agricultural and household chemicals. Then, if you have anything combustible, and plenty of water and a way to disperse it, go ahead and burn what you can, but make absolutely, positively certain the fire is out before you leave. "Out" in this case means cold to the touch.

You may be able to use, or otherwise recycle, part of the remainder, and the rest you can take home to add to your home garbage-collection schedule, perhaps over a short period of time rather than all at once.

Bush-hogging: To make the place look its very best, bush-hog any brush small enough to be cut. If the place doesn't sell quickly, do it every few weeks.

Closing the Sale:

Now you're all set to go. When you find a buyer, and *after* he's given you money and signed your contract, it's time to prepare for the closing.

I strongly suggest that you be ready to get him to sign and notarize all the documents required at the very beginning of the deal, even though if you follow my suggestions, you won't be recording most of them for six months.

Good Luck!

Appendix A: Common Corner Markings

Public Land Survey Pin: This is the state-of-the art today. That is, if you order a private survey, here's what's most likely to result. This is a plastic cap on a half or three-eighths inch rebar. Note the surveyor's name and the number of the survey.

Public Land Survey Pin: Metal cap style using the surveyor's initials and the year instead of the name

U.S.G.S. Marker: The U.S. Government uses corner markers like this. Engravings vary. Note the "Unlawful to Disturb" comment. It is a federal offense to remove or tamper with any survey marker, not just ones from government agencies, so don't mess with them.

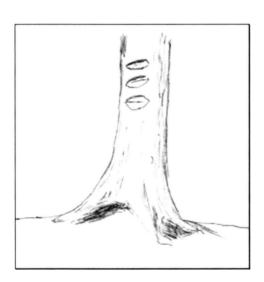

Witness Tree or Bearing Tree: Three blazes is the sign of a witness tree, which marks either a corner, or a spot close to a corner. You don't find so many of these any more.

Witness Tree Sign: Signs like this are often found on witness trees which monument government corners.

The Army Corps of Engineers uses white paint and white "T"-posts to mark the borders of government property (along COE lake take-lines, for example). National Forest boundaries are commonly marked with white or blue paint.

Rebar: A pretty common sight is rebar used as a corner marker. The fact that this one is askew suggests it should have been longer and/or set deeper.
Also common-place are steel pipe, T-posts and, from back when cars were simpler, old solid-beam axles.

Pile of Rocks: No, really. This is still the most common form of corner marking in most rural areas, and just because they're crude and cheap doesn't mean they aren't accurate - necessarily. Whenever you find one, add a rock to it before you leave.

One of the most interesting corner markers I've ever found was in Stone County Missouri. In reading the abstract to the property, I found a reference in a 19th century deed to a corner marked with a single rock, and it gave the dimensions of said stone. I thought that sounded interesting, as how could one be certain that he had the right rock and not a pretender of the approximate same size? Well, I went out into the woods and found the corner and sure enough, there was this piece of limestone half or two-thirds buried in the ground with a neat "x" chiseled onto the top 150 years ago. No question about it, this was the rock I was looking for.

Appendix B: Typical Examples of Documents Discussed in this Book

What follows are common examples of the legal documents commonly used in real estate transactions. These are only intended as examples, which I chose for their simplicity, common phrasing, and because they provide good basic protections to land sellers and buyers as opposed to those transferring title to more improved properties. However, you are not me, and I am not an attorney, therefore you should not copy these documents to use in actual real estate transactions unless approved by your attorney, who will almost certainly prefer to write or refer his or her own. Rather, I suggest you become familiar with these forms, and learn the elements of each because each land transaction will have at least some of them. I'll tag along with you and make a few comments in green:

Notice that marital status is made very clear in each document. It is very important that anyone who has interest in a property is mentioned on all the deeds, lest a "cloud" be created on the title. Even if you aren't living in a community property state, get the names of both spouses and anyone else who may have title interest in the property

The Contract for Deed defines the deal and obligates the principles to deliver their end of the agreement. Contracts of this type shouldn't be recorded and so aren't notarized. The first payment that the contract calls for is known as the earnest money, since it demonstrates that the buyer is earnest, that is, how serious he is in fact it even defines exactly how earnest he is and gives it a dollar figure. So, as seller, if you have a prospect that sounds really good, but you don't get any earnest money, don't kid yourself, you don't have a sale.

Contract For Deed

This agreement, made this day, April 16, 2011, by and between Elmer and Selma Seller, husband and wife, hereafter referred to as "the sellers", and Byron and Barbara Buyer, husband and wife, the buyer(s), hereinafter referred to as "you".

LET IT BE KNOWN that for the consideration hereinafter specified, the sellers hereby sell, and agree to convey to you, the following described land situated in the County of Marion and State of Arkansas to-wit:

All of the East Half of the East Half of the Southeast Quarter of the Northeast Quarter of the Southeast Quarter of Section 37, Township 28 North, Range 14 West,

INCLUDING ALL RIGHTS to the water and timber thereon; all rights to, or a controlling interest in, the minerals thereon, and right of legal access, subject to all easements and restrictions of record.

IN CONSIDERATION WHEREOF, you hereby promise to pay to the Sellers One Hundred Twenty-three Thousand, Four Hundred Fifty-six and 78/100 Dollars ($10.00), as follows: One Thousand, Two Hundred and Fifty-two 18/100 Dollars ($1,252.18) in hand, the receipt of which is hereby acknowledged, and One Thousand, Two Hundred and Fifty-two 18/100 Dollars ($1,252.18) on or before the same day of each of the next five succeeding months together with interest at NINE per cent per.

Payment shall first be applied to the interest accrued to the date of payment and the remainder to the principal. Interest ninety days in arrears shall be compounded daily. At the end of 180 days from this date, if you have paid the above mentioned six installments, Sellers will pass title to you by General Warranty Deed in exchange for your promise to pay the remaining balance of the sale price as documented by a Promissory Note and Deed of Trust which will supersede this contract.

In this Contract, the sellers have agreed to finance the buyers for the given monthly payment. After six months of consecutive, timely payments, they will record a Warranty Deed in the buyer's name, and take back (hold) the recorded Deed of Trust, and the Promissory Note as security. Such a contract may be made to reward the buyer with title at any time, including after all payments have been made, but putting the transfer of title far into the future is fraught with hazards for the buyer.

You agree not to cut or remove marketable timber (defined as trees with a stump diameter of greater than eight inches) from the property without the express written permission the Sellers during the time this contract is in effect. Such permission shall not be unreasonably denied for on-site construction.

You agree not to allow debris to collect on the property, including but not limited to, household wastes, derelict vehicles and unused building materials. In the event that you do not remove such debris within a reasonable time, the Sellers have the right to remove and dispose of said refuse at your expense.

You agree to contract with a waste disposal company serving the area surrounding this property before establishing a residence here.

The Sellers guarantee and covenant to defend your right to legal access to this property.

You agree not to construct any buildings or locate any residence within one hundred feet of the access road(s) or within thirty feet of a boundary.

The Sellers grant you permission to keep whatever pets and livestock you desire on this property. You, in turn, agree to responsibly manage such animals so that they are not allowed to become a nuisance to neighboring properties.

You agree to pay all taxes or assessments hereinafter becoming due and payable against this land and any improvements made thereon.

On payment of the sums of money and interest aforesaid, the Sellers shall convey this land to you by a duly acknowledged deed containing a covenant that, the Sellers are well seized of said land at the date thereof, and a covenant against encumbrances, and warranting title as of date thereof.

It is expressly understood and agreed that time is the essence of this contract and that if you should fail to pay any installment, interest, taxes, lien or other payment for a period of thirty days after said payment shall become due and payable, then the amount theretofore paid by you shall, at the option of the Sellers, be forfeited to the Sellers as liquidated damages for breach of this contract, and on such default, it will be lawful and proper for the sellers, or their assigns, upon twenty days notice to you, to take possession of the said premises. Failure at times to exercise this option shall not constitute a waiver of the right to exercise it later.

If this contract or reference thereto is of record, the Sellers' affidavit of default and of delivery of mailing to you during such default, of notice of termination, shall be conclusive proof in favor of any subsequent purchasers, their heirs or assigns, for value of such default and of the termination of your rights hereunder, if such facts are not specifically contradicted by affidavit or other instrument recorded in the county before execution of any instrument conveying equitable or legal title to such purchaser, their heirs or assigns.

> Should anyone record this contract, the cloud it creates can be nullified by recording and affidavit of default.

If this contract is not signed and mailed to the sellers within ten days of receipt of same by you, then the Sellers may, at their discretion declare this contract null and void.

It is mutually agreed that all covenants and agreements herein contained shall extend to and be obligatory upon the heirs, executors, administrators, successors and assigns of the respective parties.

This contract is offered without regard to race, religion, sex or national origin.

IN WITNESS WHEREOF, the said parties have herewith set their hands and seals. Executed in duplicate.

_____Date_____
Byron Buyer

_____Date_____
Barbara Buyer

_____Date_____
Elmer Seller

_____Date_____
Selma Seller

The Warranty Deed transfers ownership of real estate from Person A to Person B and in it, Person A guarantees that he owns clear title to the property prior to the sale. Notice that the consideration is given as "One Dollar, and other valuable considerations" this can also be the full price of the property, but this variation is used frequently so as not to make the amount of the sale a matter of public record.

The "Grantee's Mailing Address" will be used to send the annual tax bill, so make certain this is the correct address where you'll be receiving mail at the end of the calendar year.

Warranty Deed

KNOW ALL MEN BY THESE PRESENTS:

That Elmer Seller and Selma Seller, husband and wife, hereafter referred to as Grantors, in consideration of One Dollar, and other valuable considerations, to them paid by Byron Buyer and Barbara Buyer, husband and wife, hereafter referred to as Grantee, [Grantee's mailing address: Route 1, Box 234, Alton, Missouri 65641] the receipt of which is hereby acknowledged, do by these presents, Grant, Bargain, Sell, Convey and Confirm unto the said Grantee, and its assigns, the following described parcel of land, lying being and situate in the County of Oregon and State of Missouri, to wit:

All of the East Half of the Southeast Quarter of the Northeast Quarter of the Northwest Quarter (E1/2 SE1/4 NE1/4 NW1/4 Section 37, Township 23 North, Range 3 West

TO HAVE AND TO HOLD the premises aforesaid, with all and singular the rights, privileges, appurtenances, and immunities thereto belonging or in anywise appertaining unto the said Grantee, and his assigns, forever, the said Grantors covenanting that he, his heirs, administrators

and assigns shall and will WARRANT AND DEFEND the title to the premises unto the Grantees, and to their heirs, administrators and assigns, forever, against the lawful claims of all persons whomsoever, excepting however, the general taxes for the calendar year of date and thereafter, and special taxes becoming a lien after the date of this deed.

In witness whereof, the said Grantors have set their hands this_____day of _ , 2039.

X _____ _Elmer Seller
X_____ Selma Seller

All documents that are to be recorded must be notarized with a notary acknowledgement like this one:

WARRANTY DEED ACKNOWLEDGEMENT)
STATE OF NORTH CAROLINA
)ss

.

County of_____   )

On this_____day of , 2015, before me personally appeared Elmer Seller and Selma Seller, husband and wife, to me known to be the persons described in and who executed the foregoing instrument, and acknowledged that they executed the same as their free act and deed.

IN TESTIMONY WHEREOF, I have hereunto set my hand and affixed my official seal, at my office in , the day and year first above written.   My term as a Notary Public will expire_____.

signature____

(print)_____, Notary Public (notary seal)

The Deed of Trust secures the Promissory Note making the property collateral for the loan. In it, the Borrower, who's already received title to the property via the Warranty Deed (which must be recorded first) is now actually giving the land to the Trustee, to hold while the Borrower fulfills his payment obligation.

Deed of Trust

This deed, made and entered into this day, June 20, 2000 by Byron Buyer, and his wife Barbara Buyer, whose mailing address is: HCR 543 Box 21Z, Mountain View, Missouri, 65528; as Lenders; and Trent Tristin, Trustee, of Phelps County, Missouri; and Elmer Seller, and his wife Selma Seller, of Howell County, Missouri, as Borrowers.

WITNESSETH, that the said Borrowers, for and in consideration of the debt and trust hereinafter mentioned and created, and the sum of One Dollar to them paid by the said Trustee, the receipt of which is hereby acknowledged, does by these presents, Grant, Bargain, Sell, Convey and confirm unto the said Trustee, the following described real estate situated in the County of Douglas and State of Missouri, to wit:

All of the East Half of the Southeast Quarter of the Northeast Quarter of the Northwest Quarter (E1/2 SE1/4 NE1/4 NW1/4 Section 37, Township 23 North, Range 3 West

TO HAVE AND TO HOLD the same with the appurtenances, to the said Trustee and to his successors hereinafter designated, and to the assigns of the same, and of their successors forever: In trust, however, for the following purposes:

WHEREAS, Borrower has this day executed and delivered to Lender their Promissory Note dated June 20, 2000 in the amount of Seven Thousand, One Hundred Thirty-five and 08/100 Dollars ($7,135.08) bearing interest at the rate of NINE per cent per annum from the date payable in monthly installments of One Hundred Thirty-three and 05/100 Dollars ($133.05) principal and interest included. Borrower reserves the right to make pre-payment at any time, in any amount, without penalty.

WHEREAS, Borrower covenants with the Trustee to pay all taxes and assessments levied on said property before any penalty for nonpayment attaches thereto: to abstain from any commission of waste upon the premises; to obey the land use restrictions of record; and in the case of failure to do so, Lender may pay such taxes or repair such waste, and the sums of money expended therefore, together with ten per cent interest thereon from date of advancement shall be secured hereby; and

WHEREAS, Borrower takes the premises as tenant of the Trustee and agrees to pay as rent, the sum of One Cent per month until default hereunder, payable on demand, and upon default, will immediately deliver peaceful possession of the property to the Trustee or his assigns, or his successor. If the said note and interest is paid when due and payable, and the aforesaid agreement is faithfully performed, then this deed shall be void and the property herein conveyed shall be released at the cost of the Borrower, but if default is made in the payment of principal or interest when either becomes due and payable, or if any of the above-named covenants are not kept and the Trustee, or her successor, when authorized to sell under these presents, and when a sale is desired by Lender, may proceed to sell the property heretofore described, or any part thereof, at public venue, to the highest bidder at the courthouse in Douglas County for cash, first giving 20 days public notice of the time, terms, and place of sale, and of the property to be sold, by advertisement in some newspaper published in the county where the property is located, and upon such sale, shall execute and deliver a deed in fee simple of the property sold, to the purchaser or purchasers thereof, and receive the proceeds of said sale out of which he shall pay first, the costs and expenses of executing this trust, including compensation to the trustee for his services, and next, the note, heretofore described, and all interest due thereon, and the remainder, if any, shall be paid to the Borrower, or the Borrower's legal representative.

The Trustee herein covenants to perform and fulfill the trust herein created. The Trustee may resign at any time upon 30 days notice or Lender may remove the Trustee and appoint a successor at any time as it sees fit.

In witness whereof, the said parties have set their hands and seals the day and year first above written.

_____

Byron Buyer

_____

Barbara Buyer

ACKNOWLEDGEMENT

STATE OF   )
County of   )

On this_____day of   , 19_____, before me personally appeared Byron Buyer and Barbara Buyer, husband and wife, to me known to be the persons described in and who executed the foregoing instrument, and acknowledged that they executed the same as their free act and deed.

IN TESTIMONY WHEREOF, I have hereunto set my hand and affixed my official seal, at my office in , the day and year first above written.

My term as a Notary Public will expire_____. signature_____
(print)_____, Notary Public (notary seal)

The Promissory note occupies a rather unusual position in that it is not notarized and recorded and thus is like chattel property. Care should be taken not to lose it, although there are simple remedies (such as an affidavit of lost note) if that should occur. The Deed of Trust is said to "secure" payment of the Promissory Note.

February 9, 2090

Promissory Note

For value received, the undersigned, jointly and severally as principals agree to pay to the order of Elmer and Selma Seller, the sum of Twenty-six Thousand, Five Hundred and 00/100 Dollars ($26,500.00) with interest thereon from date at the rate of NINE per cent per annum, said principal and interest to be paid in multiple monthly installments as follows: Two Hundred

Sixty-eight and 78/100 Dollars ($268.78), on March 9, 2010, and a like amount on the same day of each succeeding month thereafter until paid in full. Each of such payments to be applied first in payment of interest due on the entire unpaid principal, with interest after maturity at the rate of NINE per cent per annum on the principal.

If default be made in any of said monthly installments when due, the holder of this note may at the option of said holder declare all unpaid indebtedness evidenced by this note immediately due and payable, and thereupon the undersigned agree to pay all costs of collections. Failure at times to exercise such option shall not constitute a waiver of the right to exercise it later.

In the event default be made in the payment of any monthly installment, when due, and the holder of this note does not exercise its option to declare all unpaid indebtedness due and payable, the undersigned agree to pay, during the period of delinquency, interest on the unpaid balance of the loan at the rate of nine per cent per annum.

The holder may arrange, adjust, and extend the times and amounts of payment of interest and/or principal of this note by agreement with the present or subsequent owner of the real estate securing same, without notice to or consent of and without releasing any party liable hereon.

Multiple installments may be paid on any date installments are due.

X   Byron Buyer
X   Barbara Buyer

Holding this Quit-claim Deed as additional collateral is a good idea, but the holder should understand that the Borrower may cause liens on the title which would require foreclosure of the Deed of Trust to erase. The Lender should be very careful that no such liens exist before he releases the Deed of Trust.

Quit-claim Deed

(To be held in escrow and recorded only in the event of default on a certain Deed of Trust and Promissory Note of even date.)

This deed made and entered into this day, January 22, 2002 by and between Byron Buyer and Barbara Buyer, husband and wife, Grantor, and Elmer Seller and Selma Seller, husband and wife of Howell County Missouri, Grantee.

Witnesseth: that the said Grantor, in consideration of the sum of One Dollar, and other valuable considerations paid by the Grantee, the receipt of which is hereby acknowledged, does by these presents, remise, release, and forever quit-claim unto the said party of the second part and its assigns, the following described parcel of land lying, being and situate in the county of Marion and state of Arkansas to-wit:

All of the East Half of the Southeast Quarter of the Northeast Quarter of the Northwest Quarter (E1/2 SE1/4 NE1/4 NW1/4 Section 37, Township 23 North, Range 3 West

TO HAVE AND TO HOLD the premises aforesaid, with all and singular the rights, privileges, appurtenances, and immunities thereto belonging unto the said party of the second part, its assigns, forever, so that neither the said party of the first part nor their heirs, nor any other person or persons for them or in their name or behalf, shall or will hereafter claim or demand any right or title to the aforesaid premises, or any part thereof, but they and everyone of them shall by these presents be excluded and forever barred.

IN WITNESS WHEREOF the said parties of the first part of hereunto set their hands the day and year first above written.

_____

Byron Buyer

_____

Barbara Buyer

ACKNOWLEDGEMENT:

STATE OF _   )
) ss.
County of __   )

On this_____day of   , 2031, before me personally appeared Byron Buyer and Barbara Buyer, husband and wife, to me known to be the persons described in and who executed the foregoing instrument, and acknowledged that they executed the same as their free act and deed.

IN TESTIMONY WHEREOF, I have hereunto set my hand and affixed my official seal, at my office in_____, the day and year first above written.

My term as a Notary Public will expire ._
signature_____Public (print)____, Notary (notary seal)

Glossary

Adverse possession: Acquiring legal title to land without compensating the previous owner. Often the ultimate solution to boundary disputes. Your physical possession of the property must have been actual, open and notorious, exclusive, adverse, and continuous for the statutory period. Rules defining adverse possession vary widely in different states and countries.

Air drainage: The tendency of cooling air to flow from higher to lower elevation, perhaps creating frost pockets in valleys

Amortization: A calculation that determines a specific monthly (or other periodic) sum required to retire a loan in a given period of months, or years, while paying the same amount with each payment.

Aquifer: A body of permeable rock in which water moves easily through the pores in the rock. This movement filters the water removing contaminates, viruses, and bacteria.

Arable: Suitable for producing tillage, farming and producing crops.

Artesian: Said of a well or spring in which water originating from an water table at a higher elevation than that of the well or spring, so that there is sufficient pressure to force water to the surface.

Assessor's Office: The county Assessor's Office is responsible for assessing taxes against each individual tract of land. As such, this office is the place to visit to learn the ownership of any given parcel of land.

Baseline: In the <u>Public Land Survey System</u>, a baseline is a principal east-west parallel line which corresponds with north-south Principle Meridian lines. Baselines divide survey townships into north and south.

Bottom-land: Low-lying areas where top-soil accumulates.

Chain of title: The history of ownership for a particular tract of land; chains of title usually begin with the original land patent or grant from the government and continue through all owners up to the present.

Chattel: All types of property except real estate.

Clear title: Title to property which is free of all liens, defects and clouds.

Cloud on title: The fact or appearance of a flaw in the chain of title which, if true would divide the ownership of a property and limit the marketability of the land. A cloud can be cured by presenting acceptable documented evidence disproving the cloud, or by a quiet-title suit.

Collector's Office: The county Collector's Office is responsible for collecting all taxes assessed in the county. This is the office you'll be working with if you plan to bid at a Collector's Sale (for unpaid taxes).

Deed of Trust: Essentially this is a mortgage in which a neutral third party, the trustee, stands between the lender and the borrower. In the event of default, the trustee performs the foreclosure.

Default: Failure to meet the terms of a Deed of Trust or mortgage as specifically defined in that instrument, not simply being late with a payment.

Divining or "dowsing: The belief that water, buried metals, oil or other substances or materials can be found by actions such as holding two sticks in a certain fashion until one or both of them moves, apparently on its own. There is no scientific evidence that divining is any more accurate that random chance.

Fixtures: In real estate law, a fixture is anything permanently affixed to real property so that it becomes part of the property rather than remaining chattel and it's removal would devalue the real property in questions. Good examples would be buildings, wells and fencing.

Frontage: In residential real estate, this usually means the front of a subdivided lot where the access road adjoins the parcel. In the rural-land business however, frontage can refer to that boundary shared with a roadway, or a stream of water.

Lien: An encumbrance on property representing the debt of a specific amount of money. Liens may originate voluntarily, as when a borrower mortgages his property, or involuntarily, as in the case of a tax lien, or mechanic's lien.

Meridian (Principal): In the <u>Public Land Survey System</u>, a Principal Meridian is the north-south parallel (or nearly parallel) line which corresponds with east-west baselines.

Mortgage: A debt secured by real property between a lender and a borrower, without the use of a trustee.

Notary acknowledgement: An oath given, signed and sealed by a licensed Notary Public acknowledging the signatures on legal documents. Deeds and other instruments must be notarized in order to be recorded at the county.

Prescriptive easement: An easement across the property of another, without that person's permission, which has continued long enough for the state to recognize its existence.

Quieting title: When all other ways to clear title are unavailable, the quiet-title suit is the ultimate solution. It calls for anyone making any claim to the property to respond to the court in timely fashion or lose their claim.

Quit-claim Deed: Transfers ownership of property, if any, from one owner to another. The person making the deed may, or may not, own any interest in the property at all, but whatever interest they do own is transferred by this deed without making any guarantee that any such ownership exists.

Real property: All land plus any buildings or other fixtures which have become permanently attached to the property. The opposite of chattel property

Recorder's Office: The county Recorder's Office, in addition to keeping birth, death and marriage records, keeps a copy of every deed, affidavit and survey pertinent to any real property. Ownership of land does not become official until a deed has been recorded a the Recorder's Office.

Second mortgage: A second, or subsequent debt secured by a previously encumbered property. In the event of default on a second or "subordinate" loan, the lender has a right to foreclose the borrower, but should the lender take over possession of the property from the borrower when a first, or "superior" is owed, then the lender must assume, or pay, the first lien.

Title insurance: An insurance policy guaranteeing title to a particular piece of real property.

Title search: The research required to determine good title to land. Different from title insurance in that no guarantee is made of the accuracy of the search, or the marketability of the property.

Topsoil: The top layer of soil containing much humus and organic material, as opposed to the sub-soil which contains clay-ey, inorganic material. Topsoil is a requirement for proper plant growth.

Warranty Deed: Conveys ownership of property from a grantor to a grantee. In making an Warranty Deed, the owner not only conveys his title to the buyer, he also guarantees that his title is good.

Watershed: The land from which rainwater drains to form any particular stream. A watershed can be large, such as the Mississippi River basin, or as small as the area that feeds a stock pond.

Witness tree: In the earlier days of land surveying, these blazed trees were used to mark corners or boundaries, at least as long as the tree remained standing.

About the Author

Neil Shelton has enjoyed a career in real estate spanning over four decades, first as a broker, when he was a leading player in the 70's back-to-the-land boom, and later, as a major innovator in rural land sales, who created *OzarkLand.com,* the internet's first website allowing purchasers to buy land online.

Additionally, he is the creator and publisher of *Homestead.org: The Homesteader's Free Library*, and author of *The Everything Backyard Farming Book* (F+W Media Inc. 2013).

He and his wife Olga live in an undisclosed location deep inside the Ozark forest.

Made in the USA
Lexington, KY
23 June 2016